The Design and Operation of Small Sewage Works

Bo.... ....

The Design and Operation of Small Sewage Works

D. Barnes
School of Civil Engineering,
University of New South Wales, Australia

and

F. Wilson
Department of Civil Engineering,
University of Canterbury,
Christchurch, New Zealand

Both formerly of
Department of Civil Engineering,
University of Strathclyde,
Glasgow.

E. & F. N. SPON LTD.
LONDON
A Halsted Press book
John Wiley & Sons, New York

P.J.Pڊd

First published in 1976
by E. & F. N. Spon Ltd.
11 New Fetter Lane, London EC4P 4EE

Typeset by Santype International Ltd,
(Coldtype Division), Salisbury, Wilts.
and printed in Great Britain
by Cambridge University Press

ISBN 0 419 10980 3

Contents

Preface

This book has evolved from the teaching of Public Health Engineering to undergraduate and postgraduate students at the University of Strathclyde and particularly from a series of short courses dealing with sewage treatment and sludge disposal for small and variable communities. In August 1973 a request was received from the Forestry Commission to provide an intensive course dealing with aspects of sewage treatment relevant to the camping and caravan sites and the forest villages under their control. A week long course was mounted in March 1974 which was attended by members of the Forestry Commission and several representatives from local authorities, consultants, public authorities and commercial firms. The response to the minimal publicity indicated that the course met a demand for knowledge and was subsequently repeated in September 1974 and June 1975. Publication of the course as a book was a logical method of extension of the short courses.

The courses and the book were not intended to provide a summary of current research into waste treatment processes; instead it is intended to provide practical assistance in the choice, construction and maintenance of a small treatment plant. It is therefore hoped that the book will serve as a useful guide during the choice, installation and operation of any small plant. In real terms this often means the choice between package plants supplied by specific manufacturers employing various treatment processes and the local construction of a small sewage works. It is obviously impossible to make any definitive recommendation to meet local conditions — otherwise the book would be redundant, or very brief. Instead, it is intended to convey the basic principles of treatment processes and to point out the advantages, disadvantages, difficulties and limitations of particular processes.

It is appreciated that the book may be read by people with widely differing backgrounds and engineering experience. In order to help those who are meeting the subject of sanitary engineering for the first time, certain chapters have been written to give a general introduction to the subject, e.g. Chapters 1, 2, 3. Other chapters have been written to aid those who are more particularly engaged in the design or construction of small sewage treatment works, e.g. Chapter 4.

The processes occurring in sewage treatment are often taught from a unit operations approach where individual processes or operations are discussed separately. Chapters 7 to 11 are based on this method. It is hoped, however, that the partial repetition of important points throughout the book will prevent the compartmentalization of the subject often engendered by this approach.

The chapters dealing with legal and constructional aspects of small works are

xi

intended to help the educated layman, as also is the chapter on pumping. No book on small sewage treatment works would be complete without reference to chemical methods of sanitation. The widespread use of such methods of sanitation provides serious problems for many small scale works, especially camping and caravan site waste treatment. Chapter 5 therefore discusses this 'unmentionable' subject and also anticipates the possible future use of physico-chemical treatment processes for wastewater treatment.

In the course of preparing the book, the authors were contacted by many people, working in the field of small scale sewage treatment, concerning the problems of design and operation of small works in hot climates. The recent realization, in Britain, of the vast potential of export sales to middle eastern countries has led to an increase in the need for information on this subject which is only matched by its paucity. Chapter 16 has, therefore, been written with the intention of providing a background to this subject – which subject is probably deserving of a whole book to itself. The authors have, therefore, had little choice but to select the more important points.

The case of package plants is particularly difficult. During the short courses, various manufacturers gave lectures outlining their products and provided outline specifications to meet case studies which we prepared. This type of approach has been adopted in a modified form and is included in the book. The inclusion of manufacturers' data and prices does not constitute a recommendation by the authors for particular plant, nor are the prices or relative prices expected to remain constant.

The section of the book dealing with legal aspects has been partly co-authored by Professor J. Barnes of the Department of Law, Carleton University, Canada, and valuable suggestions were also made by Mr E. Young of the Department of Law, University of Strathclyde. Mr J. Stokes of Elsan Ltd., gave a lecture during some of the short courses and we are grateful for his advice and assistance in preparing the sections which deal with chemical sanitation. Dr W. Duncan of the Department of Civil Engineering, University of Strathclyde, wrote the chapter on Structural Design and Construction and made contributions to discussions of the structural aspects of tank construction. Mr D. Rachman of the Department of Mechanical Engineering, University of Strathclyde, wrote the chapter on Pumps and Pumping. Thanks are due to Mr W. Stuart of the Inka division of A. Johnson Construction Co. and Mr M. A. Hamadah of the Water Resources Development Centre, Kuwait for comments included in Chapter 16.

We would like to thank the firms who have contributed to the courses and the book: Ames Crosta Mills, C.J.B. Developments, Dickson Environmental Engineering, Eimco, William E. Farrer, A. Johnson Construction Company, Klargester Environmental Engineering, Motherwell Bridge Engineering, Satec, Mr C. MacMahon of the Forestry Commission, who initiated the courses, undergraduate students (Messrs. R. C. Davidson, J. M. Reddish, S. K. Rimmer, J. B. S. Stewart, J. L. Summers) and postgraduate students (Messrs A. Andreadakis, S. Ashie, F. Farah, S. Hameed, N. Katsiris and D. Wilson) who have carried out research projects on small sewage works. We would particularly like to thank Miss Rosa Stewart for her expert typing of the manuscript, Mr Phillip Read of the publishers for his active co-operation and our colleagues within the Department of Civil Engineering at the University of Strathclyde, for the congenial working environment during our period within the department. Particular thanks are due to Professor D. I. H. Barr, Head of the 'wet' section of the department, and Dr P. Coackley, Reader in Public Health Engineering and organiser of the M.Sc. course in Public Health Engineering, who has remained our mentor and friend. Finally, we thank our wives and families for their co-operation and assistance during the writing of the book.

Abbreviations used throughout this book

B.O.D.	Biochemical Oxygen Demand
B.O.D.$_5$	5 Day Biochemical Oxygen Demand
cap.	capita
C.O.D.	Chemical Oxygen Demand
d	day
D.O.	Dissolved Oxygen
D.W.F.	Dry Weather Flow
g	grams
gal	gallon
h	hour
l	litre
lb	pound (weight)
m	metres
M.C.	Moisture Content
mg/l	milligrams per litre
M.L.S.S.	Mixed Liquor Suspended Solids
R.B.F.	Rotating Biological Filter
s	second
S.V.I.	Sludge Volume Index
S.S.	Suspended Solids
T.W.L.	Top Water Level
W	Watt
30 : 20	30 mg/l S.S. and 20 mg/l B.O.D.$_5$

Definitions

Activated sludge.   A dark brown suspension of bacterial flocs produced by the aeration of sewage; prolonged aeration in admixture with this sludge effectively purifies sewage.

Baffle.   A board which dips below the T.W.L. of a tank at the inlet to disperse the flow into the tank.

Biological filter (also known as a bacteria bed or percolating filter).   A porous bed of suitable, graded, inert material. Bacteria and other organisms flourish on the surface of this material and bring about oxidation of the organic matter in the settled sewage applied to the filter.

Distributor.   A device which distributes the tank effluent evenly over the surface of the filter medium.

Dosing chamber.   A container which receives effluent from a septic tank or from a settlement tank, and from which this effluent is automatically discharged to the filter distributor, in intermittent doses.

Dry weather flow (D.W.F.).   The quantity of sewage to be treated in 24 hours, which may be regarded as equal to the water consumption for domestic purposes in the same period.

Filter medium.   The material, such as hard clinker or broken stone, with which a biological filter is filled.

Final effluent.   The liquid discharged finally from a sewage treatment works.

Five day biochemical oxygen demand (B.O.D.$_5$).   The mass of oxygen consumed by unit volume of liquid (expressed as milligrams per litre (mg/l)) during biological oxidation in the course of 5 days at 20°C.

Humus tank.   A tank, through which filter effluent is passed, to settle solids which should be removed at frequent intervals.

Rotating biological filter (R.B.F.), also known as a rotating biological contactor. Usually a series of rotating discs partially submerged in settled sewage. The discs accumulate a growth of biological material as in a biological filter, and obtain oxygen as that portion of the disc rotates through the air.

Scumboard.   A sheet of solid material which dips below the T.W.L. of a tank to prevent scum flowing out with the liquid.

Septic tank.   A tank through which sewage is passed to settle solids which are retained to undergo digestion by anaerobic bacterial action.

Settlement tank.   A tank through which sewage is passed to settle solids which should be removed at frequent intervals.

Sewage.   The discharge from domestic and sanitary appliances on premises coming within the scope of this book.

Sludge.   The slurry which is formed in a tank by deposition of settleable solids.

Supernatant liquor.   The layer of liquid overlying the settled solids which have separated from it.

Suspended solids (S.S.).   The solids which are suspended in a sewage or effluent.

T.W.L.   The top water level in a tank.

Water table.   The surface of the subsoil water.

The majority of these definitions are an extract from C.P. 302: 1972 and are reproduced by permission of the British Standards Institution, 2 Park Street, London W1A 2BS, from whom complete copies can be obtained.

1 Sewage and sewage disposal

1.1 Introduction

Traditionally, man has relied upon the natural degradation processes of micro-organisms which are present in the environment to decompose waste materials effectively. The discharge of solid and liquid waste to soil and water is an effective method of disposal provided that the load imposed upon the natural processes is not excessive.

The industrial revolution and the associated growth of urban communities created the problem of high volumes of wastes to be disposed of within confined areas without significantly destroying the local environment. The development of effective methods of sewage treatment and garbage disposal for large communities was therefore a necessity for which there are now well documented methods. More recently there has been an increasing appreciation that man made pollution is a significant national and global problem. This has led to the formation of authorities with powers to improve the qualities of waters and the imposition of stricter standards for sewage treatment.

For small communities, the most common form of sewage treatment has been the septic tank. While this mode of treatment still has a restricted use, it will rarely meet the current more stringent criteria and, therefore, more effective methods of sewage treatment are required, particularly when existing small communities expect to increase their population. Additionally, extra leisure time has increased the demands upon seasonal centres which cater predominantly for holiday activities. The growth of camping and caravan sites and of hotels distant from sewered communities has created a demand for small but flexible sewage treatment works which can still meet current effluent standards.

Sewage treatment at these types of communities presents a range of difficulties which are often extreme cases of the problems encountered at larger treatment works. The severity of these difficulties has meant that, while the principles of the processes employed in these smaller works are very similar to those in the larger works, the detailed design and operation of smaller works does differ.

The ensuing chapters are an attempt to explain the processes and problems of small sewage works, to show how the theory of the processes is related to practice, to give some guidance about the choice between different plants and the maintenance of plants. In general, sewerage and the impact of treated

1

effluents upon receiving waters are not discussed. The processes considered are restricted to those between the inlet and outlet of the sewage works. The examples and standards are principally those which are relevant to Britain, although similar considerations apply to other parts of Europe, North America and Australasia.

1.2 Origin of sewage

The communities considered are all non-industrial, and no industrial wastes are considered to be present in the sewage. The characteristics of the sewage are, therefore, those of domestic sewage. Sewage is predominantly water, often approximately 99.9% water with less than 0.1% dry solid matter. Sewage treatment involves the concentration of this small proportion of dry solid matter into a sludge of approximately 2% dry solids and an effluent of approximately 0.003% dry solids. It is therefore important to consider the origin and composition of this solid material.

Sewage originates from three major sources: washing, food preparation and excretion. The absolute minimum volume of materials produced per person per day by these processes, without any water, is less than 4 litres (4 l). However, in technologically developed countries, these absolute minimum values are greatly exceeded. The ready availability of a water supply leads to a vast dilution of the concentrated waste materials, e.g. in flush water closets which dilute volumes of less than 1 litre (l) to between 10 and 20 l, ready access to baths and showers and the availability of ample water for washing, particularly in automatic washing machines. These processes produce large volumes of dirty water which require treatment. The vast dilution of the basic components of sewage which usually contains a high proportion of solid material (>10%) produces conventional waterborne sewage of a low solids content (0.1%) but in large volumes (per capita flows of 200 l/d) which can be transported with relative ease to a treatment plant.

Of the water-borne sewage produced, approximately one third is from wash basins, showers and baths, one third from the water closet and the remaining one third from other miscellaneous operations which include washing-up, laundry, food and drink preparation.

The total volume of water-borne sewage produced per person per day will depend initially upon the volume of water used and the type of sewerage system. Water consumption varies with the availability of water supplies and the standard of living of the community. Commonly quoted figures indicate that per capita water consumption is higher in Scotland (250 l/d) than in England (180 l/d) but is much greater in the more technologically developed U.S.A. (300–900 l/d).

If there is complete separation of foul water from surface run off water (separate sewerage system), these volumes of sewage will need to be treated at the sewage works. However, considerable amounts of additional water can enter the sewers, particularly during or just after heavy rain, if surface drainage is connected to the foul water sewer (combined sewerage system). Similar increased flows occur if the sewerage system is incompletely sealed and permits the infiltration of significant volumes of groundwater.

1.3 Nature of sewage

Sewage is clearly a complex mixture of materials from varied sources. However, as a first approximation, bathroom wastewaters are predominantly soapy with small amounts of insoluble materials, kitchen wastewaters contain soap, food particles and dirty water, while wastewaters from water closets contain faeces, urine and paper. These materials can be separated conveniently on the basis of their size and solubility. Large particles may be either floating on top of the water or suspended in the water, but with a tendency to settle out; this group includes plastics, paper, grit and sticks. There are also materials in true solution in water which will include a range of soluble inorganic compounds, e.g. common salt (sodium chloride) and soluble organic compounds, e.g. sugar (sucrose). Colloids are not strictly dissolved in solution but yet show no tendency to settle from the solution; they include very small particles and large molecular species. Colloids in sewage originate from a range of sources and include inorganic materials, e.g. clays, and organic materials, e.g. gelatin.

1.4 Sewage treatment

Sewage is usually treated by a mixture of settlement and biological processes. A settlement process permits materials which are suspended in a sewage to settle to the bottom of a container and therefore to be removed from the bulk of the liquid. The longer a material is retained in the container, the greater the amount of suspended solids that will be able to settle out. Thus short retention times will only remove the largest particles, while long retention times provide greater solids removal. Biological processes convert materials in the sewage into biological cell materials which can usually be easily settled out from a solution by a settlement process.

A schematic description of biological sewage treatment processes is given in Fig. 1.1. Raw sewage arrives at the sewage works via the sewerage system of the community. The raw sewage passes through a screen, usually made of bars separated by 2–3 cm to remove large objects which may interfere with subsequent processes. Any materials which are larger in size than the separation between the bars will be trapped and can be removed and disposed of separately. The materials trapped on screens are usually floating solids – paper, wood, plastic. Once these larger objects are trapped, smaller but more obnoxious materials, e.g. faecal matter, become caught and the resultant screenings for removal are unhygienic and require prompt disposal. As an alternative at larger works, a comminutor can be employed. These machines cut up any large objects which are in the sewage. The comminuted sewage, therefore, also only contains particles of size smaller than that which would interfere with subsequent processes.

Large dense particles in sewage can damage mechanical equipment, and can

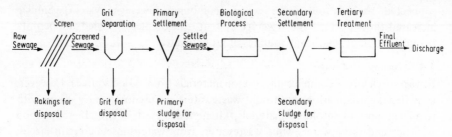

1.1   Diagrammatic representation of the processes of sewage treatment.

accumulate in subsequent treatment stages and significantly reduce the free volumes available for treatment. The largest of these particles, usually referred to as grit, are removed in a grit separator. A grit separator is designed to maintain a relatively high horizontal flow rate of sewage (approximately 0.3 m s^{-1} — see Chapter 7). At this flow rate, heavy inorganic materials will settle to the bottom of the channel, while the lighter materials remain suspended in the sewage. The grit should contain little obnoxious materials and can usually be handled and disposed of easily.

Sewage can then be subjected to a more prolonged process of settlement — primary settlement. By passing the sewage slowly through a tank, suspended solid particles settle to the floor of the tank (see Chapter 7) and can be removed as a primary sludge for separate disposal. The bulk of the liquid which will contain only soluble materials and the finer suspended solids is referred to as settled sewage (Fig. 1.1).

The materials which remain in the sewage can be converted into biological cells which settle more easily than the constituents of settled sewage. Micro-organisms can utilize the constituents of small particles and soluble materials as a food source. The major types of micro-organism responsible for consuming this food are bacteria. By providing good conditions for the growth of bacteria, e.g. ample oxygen if the bacteria require oxygen, the components of settled sewage can be converted to bacterial cells (Chapter 8). The bacterial cells can be removed from the clearer liquid by a further settlement process — secondary settlement. The overall aim of secondary settlement is similar to that of primary settlement — removal of suspended material. The secondary sludge will consist mainly of bacterial cells and again will require disposal.

In certain cases when a high quality of effluent is required, another process can be employed — tertiary treatment (Chapter 11). A range of processes are available to improve further or polish the effluent before discharge into a convenient receiving water. Effluents from a biological treatment process are usually passed through some form of filtering or straining device — a bed of sand, gravel, pebbles or soil. The structure of the filter usually traps some of the particles which remain in the effluent, and some biological processes will occur, e.g. on passing effluents through soil. A more detailed discussion of the details of the design and operation of tertiary treatment processes is given in Chapters 11 and 14. The clear liquid which should result from these processes – final effluent – can be discharged to a suitable water course or body of water.

The materials which are removed from sewage by the settlement processes are referred to as sludges. With all types of sewage treatment process, it is necessary to arrange for a hygienic and convenient method for disposal of the sludges (Chapter 10). For all types of sewage treatment process, it is important to realize that little real purification can occur. The processes are essentially those of separation. The pollutants originally present in the sewage are concentrated into the sludge, while the remaining liquid contains few pollutants.

1.5 Small scale sewage treatment

The general description of sewage treatment given in Fig. 1.1 covers the majority of treatment processes. For particular communities, this scheme is modified to account for particular circumstances. For small communities, the ubiquitous demands of low cost and high purity effluents are further complicated by considerations of maintenance, labour and size. Small communities often necessitate cheap, robust, compact sewage works which require little maintenance and can be installed and operated with unskilled labour. While no works can fully meet these varied constraints, certain modifications of the generalized sewage treatment process can operate satisfactorily.

In order to provide minimum maintenance and to reduce size and costs, several of the processes outlined previously are omitted or amalgamated. Many processes, e.g. sludge removal, are carried out on an intermittent basis rather than continuously. Tertiary treatment is rarely included in small sewage works; the additional costs are usually prohibitively high. The processes of grit separation and primary settlement can be amalgamated and, for certain processes, omitted completely. The inclusion of a hand raked screen has to be excluded if a process expects to receive only spasmodic attention.

A range of possibilities exists for the small scale treatment of sewage, and these options will be discussed briefly.

1.5.1 Septic tanks

A septic tank includes principally the processes of grit separation and primary settlement. Raw sewage is passed directly into a water-tight structure which has sufficient capacity to permit a long period of settlement (Fig. 1.2). A significant proportion of the suspended solids settle to the floor of the tank and the effluent can be discharged. Septic tanks are designed to include sufficient capacity to permit the storage of the sludge for several months. During this long period of storage, some biological action occurs, mainly in the settled sludge. The resultant sludge is removed on an annual basis. To minimize maintenance, no screen is usually included within the plant.

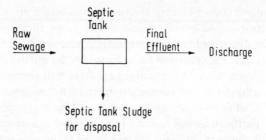

1.2   Diagrammatic representation of sewage treatment by a septic tank.

1.5.2   Biological filters

More complete treatment is provided by passing the effluent from a septic tank over a bed of hard medium — a percolating filter. The surfaces of the medium become covered with a film of microbiological organisms. These micro-organisms metabolise components of the sewage. Excessive growths of the biological film fall away from the solid surface of the medium and are separated in a secondary settlement process. This final settlement tank is often referred to as a humus tank, if it receives liquids from a percolating filter (Fig. 1.3).

Several simple alternatives are possible. Instead of passing septic tank effluents over a bed of hard media, the effluents can be passed into a tank through which partially immersed discs are rotated — rotating biological filter (Fig. 1.3). The growth of microbiological organisms and the sloughing off of film occurs on these discs in a similar manner to the percolating filter. As a further alternative, the septic tank can be replaced by a primary settlement tank for a percolating filter or for a rotating biological disc plant (Fig. 1.3). This is usually more appropriate for sewage works of moderate size. Screens are more usually employed in plants which include primary settlement tanks rather than for septic tank installations.

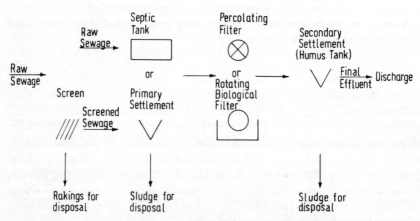

1.3   Diagrammatic representation of sewage treatment by biological filter processes.

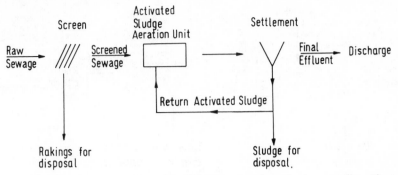

1.4   Diagrammatic representation of sewage treatment at a small activated sludge plant.

1.5.3   Activated sludge plants

Sewage is added to a concentrated suspended mixture of micro-organisms, mainly bacterial cells, and the mixture is aerated by an external source — usually by air bubbles from a compressor. The highly active mixture of micro-organisms — activated sludge — metabolises the components of sewage and so produces more activated sludge. The sludge is settled in a settlement tank. A high proportion of the sludge is returned to the inlet of the aeration unit to be mixed with fresh sewage and so maintain the required high concentration of active micro-organisms — return activated sludge (Fig. 1.4). The remaining sludge has to be disposed of. For small works, it is usual to pass screened sewage directly into the aeration unit without any primary settlement stage. Certain plants pass unscreened sewage into the aeration plant and site a screen prior to the settlement tank. Larger works incorporate separate primary settlement tanks.

Certain commercial manufacturers market sewage treatment plants which incorporate these separate processes within a compact unit. The majority of these 'package plants' which are currently available are based upon the principles of the activated sludge process. The design, operation and performance of these units should be similar to those of locally constructed works.

1.5.4   Non biological sewage treatment processes

Sewage treatment processes are available which do not rely upon a biological growth stage. Instead, a chemical is added to trap, enmesh and precipitate the very small suspended solids which will not settle under the normal conditions of a settlement process. The addition of coagulant chemical is followed by a period of gentle stirring (flocculation) to facilitate the conversion of the small particles into a larger floc (Fig. 1.5). Settlement of this mixture produces a sludge for disposal which contains the chemicals added to coagulate the suspended solid particles and an effluent which contains very little suspended solids. The process can therefore be considered as a more effective form of primary settlement. It

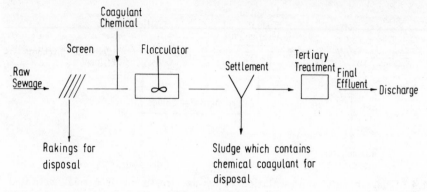

1.5   Diagrammatic representation of sewage treatment by addition of chemical coagulant.

may be necessary to carry out a tertiary treatment process to reduce the concentration of soluble compounds in the effluent prior to discharge.

Chemicals are also marketed which effectively kill all bacteria which could occur, particularly in sewage from water closets and urinals. Addition of these chemicals, therefore, sterilises the sewage and renders it more amenable to storage. This can only be a temporary expedient, and the resultant liquids require separate effective treatment or disposal. This latter process is of obvious importance in mobile dwellings, e.g. caravans, and in very remote or isolated dwellings. The addition of these sterilising chemicals as a method of chemical sanitation is discussed in Chapters 4 and 5.

1.6   Aerobic and anaerobic processes

The presence or absence of oxygen in any water, sewage or sludge will influence the type of micro-organisms which can exist in that liquid and so will influence the reactions which can occur. Any liquid, which contains oxygen dissolved in the liquid is described as aerobic. Anaerobic conditions exist in liquids which do not contain any dissolved oxygen. In all cases it is important to stress that the oxygen referred to is that present in, or absent from, the liquid. This difference is used to classify the processes of sewage treatment and the micro-organisms which are responsible for that treatment. The activated sludge process is an aerobic treatment process and relies upon aerobic micro-organisms (aerobes) to carry out any transformations. It is therefore necessary to ensure that an adequate supply of oxygen is available throughout the process. The major biological changes, therefore, occur in a tank which is aerated and mixed by an external supply of air. Septic tanks rely upon anaerobic bacteria to reduce sludge volumes. Septic tanks, therefore, do not have any aeration facilities.

1.7   Types of micro-organisms

In most sewage treatment processes, a highly complex fluctuating population of organisms exists. More detailed texts should be consulted for accurate definition and identification of the individual types of micro-organisms. The classification which follows is intended to give an indication of the nomenclature and more significant differences between organisms rather than to provide an exhaustive microbiological analysis. Some selection has been made to include only organisms which are likely to be relevant to small scale works.

1.7.1 Bacteria

Bacteria are the most important and most abundant group of micro-organisms in biological sewage treatment processes. Different types of bacteria can exist as aerobes, anaerobes or facultative bacteria. The latter type will function aerobically if oxygen is present in the solution, and anaerobically if oxygen is absent from the solution. Bacteria are the only micro-organisms which will function under anaerobic conditions and are usually the predominant micro-organisms in aerobic processes. The most important characteristics of bacteria in sewage treatment processes are:

i) Bacteria are small, less than 1 μm in diameter and less than 5 μm in length, depending upon the particular species or form. Very large numbers can exist in very small volumes of liquid.

ii) Growth rates can be very large. Consequently, the consumption of food by the bacteria can be very large and the conversion of sewage materials into bacterial cells can be rapid.

iii) Bacteria can utilize soluble substances as food sources.

iv) Many types can form extra-cellular capsules or slimes which can change the settlement characteristics of the bacteria and of higher organisms. The production of bacteria with good settlement properties is necessary for the effective separation of the bacteria in a subsequent settlement process.

1.7.2 Fungi

Fungi are multicellular, non photosynthetic plants which use organic matter as a food source. They metabolise similar materials to that of bacteria but require less nitrogen and can grow at lower pH values. Fungi are larger than bacteria and are filamentous; they have poorer settling properties than bacteria – it is therefore usual to discourage the formation of fungi in sewage treatment processes.

1.7.3 Protozoa

Protozoa are single celled animals which can utilize solid substances and reproduce by simple division. This group includes types which are motile, e.g. free swimming ciliates, and non-motile forms, e.g. stalked ciliates. Protozoa can utilize bacteria as a food source, so are important in sewage treatment processes, as they help to maintain a balanced population. Protozoa become more predominant in waters which contain less organic pollution. Thus, in any sequential sewage treatment process, the first stages rely almost entirely upon bacteria, while in later stages protozoa become more evident.

1.7.4   Rotifers and higher organisms

Rotifers are multicellular higher organisms which have rotating cilia or hairs which appear to push or waft food particles into their sac-like bodies. Rotifers graze the less complex organisms, but as they are a more complex animal, they require a stable, well aerated environment.

Worms and larvae are the most significant of the remaining higher organisms. They are important in percolating filters, as they have an influence in maintaining the void spaces between stones. The worms and larvae exist in the upper layers of a percolating filter, where they graze other organisms. Their movement deeper into the bed during the winter can adversely affect the purification efficiency of the filter.

Suggested further reading

[1] *River Pollution 3: Control*, L. Klein, Butterworths, London, 1966.
[2] *Microbiology for Sanitary Engineers*, R. E. McKinney, McGraw Hill, New York, 1962.
[3] *An Introduction to Sewage Treatment*, Inst. Water Pollution Control, London, 1968.
[4] *Principles of Water Quality Control*, T. H. Y. Tebbutt, Pergamon, Oxford, 1973.
[5] *Bacteriology for Sanitary Engineers*, D. D. Mara, Churchill Livingstone, Edinburgh, 1974.

2 Characterization and measurement of sewage, effluents and sludges

It is necessary to have standard methods of analysis to assess quantitatively the pollutional load of waters, sewages, sludges and effluents. Such analyses form the basis of design criteria for sewage treatment plants, and are used to check efficiencies of purification, effluent quality and receiving water capacities. A detailed description of the principles and procedures for such analyses is beyond the scope of this book. It is, however, of value to consider the more important tests which are carried out[1] and their application to small scale sewage treatment.

The usual method for the determination of the pollutional load of a sample is to measure the oxygen demand which the sample would exert during oxidation of the polluting material. Three general methods are available for the determination of this demand −

    a) Bacterial (biochemical oxygen demand)

    b) Chemical (chemical oxygen demand, permanganate value)

    c) Instrumental (total oxygen demand, total organic carbon).

Determination of the biochemical oxygen demand requires a method for the determination of dissolved oxygen concentration. Additionally, it is of advantage to have some knowledge of the dissolved oxygen concentration and the suspended solids content in a sample. For the operation of an activated sludge type of installation, an assessment of the settlement characteristics of the activated sludge floc is necessary (sludge volume index or sludge density index). The mode of disposal of waste sludges depends upon their type and quantity. An estimate of the ease of removing water from the sludges is often advantageous.

2.1 Determination of dissolved oxygen (D.O.)

The biological processes which are responsible for the oxidation of organic materials in water take the oxygen which they require for this process from oxygen which is dissolved in the water. The actual amount of oxygen which can dissolve in a particular sample depends upon the temperature of the sample, the pressure of oxygen in contact with the sample and the materials dissolved or suspended in the water. Normally, the maximum (saturation) concentration of dissolved oxygen in water is about 9 mg/l. This relatively low concentration of oxygen is critical for the respiration of small and large organisms. The depletion of this concentration is often the limiting factor in the purification of sewage. The determination of dissolved oxygen is, therefore, one of the most important analyses in public health engineering.

Two methods are widely employed for the determination of the D.O. levels: the Winkler chemical method[1] and the instrumental D.O. meter. The simple Winkler procedure converts dissolved oxygen into dissolved iodine by addition of manganous sulphate potassium iodide and acid. The iodine can be easily determined by titration and is directly related to the original D.O. concentration. This procedure is rather lengthy and requires some laboratory expertise; it has, however, been widely employed. Commercial electroanalytical instruments are available which record the oxygen concentration in waters. The electrodes are covered by a membrane which is permeable to oxygen. Oxygen which crosses this membrane is reduced at an electrode and the current so generated can be related to the concentration of oxygen in the solution. The instruments require calibration against a solution saturated with air and the membranes of the electrode are prone to fouling. The instruments are reliable and provide a relatively simple and quick method of directly monitoring D.O. concentrations.

2.2   Determination of pollutional load

2.2.1   Biochemical oxygen demand (B.O.D.)

This test relies upon bacteria using oxygen dissolved in the water to oxidize the organic matter in a given sample[1]. The amount of oxygen consumed during a fixed time period is related to the amount of organic material present in the original sample. The normal time period for this reaction is five days and the result is usually expressed as a five day B.O.D. – 'B.O.D.$_5$'. For a simple case, e.g. a clean aerated river water of less than 7 mg/l B.O.D.$_5$, it is merely necessary to fill two bottles with the sample – analyse the contents of one bottle immediately for dissolved oxygen (D.O.$_0$) and incubate the other sample bottle at $20°$C for five days. After incubation, the dissolved oxygen concentration is determined (D.O.$_5$). The difference between the two dissolved oxygen values (D.O.$_0$ – D.O.$_5$) gives the five day B.O.D. expressed as B.O.D.$_5$ mg/l.

In practice it is rare that such a simple procedure will be possible. It is usually necessary to carry out a series of dilutions of the original sample to ensure that an accurate measure of the oxygen depletion can be made. 30–80% depletion of the original dissolved oxygen will give a more accurate B.O.D.$_5$ determination than percentage reductions outside this range. The sample is diluted with dilution water which contains reasonable quantities of inorganic nutrients to ensure adequate biological growth, but will not exert a significant oxygen demand. It is then necessary to determine separately the dissolved oxygen concentration at time zero and to incubate the diluted sample and blanks which contain dilution water and any necessary biological seed materials. From the determinations of the dissolved oxygen concentrations after five days' incubation, the B.O.D.$_5$ can be computed.

The rate at which any chemical compound will be oxidized by microorganisms will depend upon the structure of the compound. Each compound, therefore, has a particular rate of decomposition with a specific type of micro-organism. Under the conditions of the B.O.D.$_5$ test, domestic sewage is normally 65–85% oxidized during the five day period. This degree of oxidation is, however, the overall percentage of oxidation made up from the large number of different compounds which constitute domestic sewage. The overall rate includes some compounds, e.g. simple sugars, which will be more than 90% oxidized and some compounds which are resistant to biological oxidation, e.g. oils, complex synthetic organic compounds which might be less than 10% oxidized (Fig. 2.1).

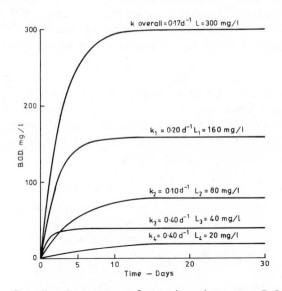

2.1   Overall and component factors in carbonaceous B.O.D.

The variation of B.O.D. with time is expressed [2] –

$$\text{B.O.D. at time } t = L \left(1 - 10^{-kt}\right)$$

Where

    k is termed the rate constant

    L is the ultimate demand for oxygen if the process were continued indefinitely.

The value of k specifies the rate of oxidation; for easily degraded samples, k will be large ($>0.3\ d^{-1}$); for compounds which are resistant to biodegradation, k will be small ($<0.05\ d^{-1}$). Domestic sewage is a mixture of many compounds (Fig. 2.1) and the observed rate constant is often about $0.17\ d^{-1}$; thus for B.O.D.$_5$ of 200 mg/l the ultimate B.O.D. (L) would be 234 mg/l — 85% of the oxidation being completed during the first five days (Fig. 2.1). For normal domestic sewages in the U.K., the B.O.D.$_5$ would normally be within the range 250—450 mg/l, while that of final effluents from a sewage treatment works would be expected to be between 10 and 50 mg/l.

In practice, the simple B.O.D. against time curve (Fig. 2.1) is not observed. Instead, a second curve, usually of comparable oxygen demand, is observed (Fig. 2.2). This additional oxygen demand is required for the oxidation of nitrogen species in the sample. The organic nitrogen originally in sewage mainly as protein molecules is degraded with the consumption of oxygen to form ammonia (NH_3) and finally nitrate ions (NO_3^-). The formation of nitrate ions therefore represents the full oxidation of organic nitrogen and this process is referred to as nitrification. In sewage samples, nitrification does not normally begin until day 8—10 of a B.O.D. test. The B.O.D.$_5$ value therefore reflects with some accuracy the ultimate carbonaceous B.O.D. of the sample. In samples which have received partial biological treatment, nitrification can begin within a much shorter time period.

The total demand for oxygen will need to be satisfied eventually for all wastes. In an efficient, effective sewage treatment plant which produces a well nitrified effluent, the oxygen requirements for the oxidation of carbonaceous material and for nitrification are met within the plant. If only the carbonaceous oxidation stage is completed within the plant, the oxygen demand for nitrification will occur in the receiving water.

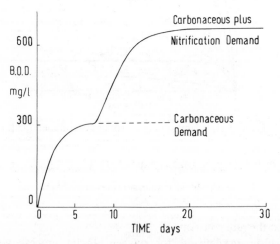

2.2   Biochemical oxygen demand curve — carbonaceous and nitrification demands.

Although subject to experimental and theoretical limitations, the B.O.D.$_5$ test is widely used and is very similar to the biological processes which are likely to be employed for the decomposition of the wastes. The measurement gives no specific information about the nature or composition of the sample, only the oxygen demand after five days of incubation at 20°C.

2.2.2   Chemical oxygen demands

Chemical oxidizing agents can be added to samples in an attempt to oxidize chemically the material contained in the samples. The degree of oxidation will depend upon the nature of the sample, the reaction time and the oxidizing powers of the reagent added. Such a measurement is related less to actual biological processes than the B.O.D. determination but is quicker and is less prone to the bacteriological problems associated with the B.O.D.$_5$ test.

Chemical oxygen demand (C.O.D.) usually refers to the amount of potassium dichromate consumed by the sample[1]. This strong oxidant is normally used for 2 hours in boiling concentrated sulphuric acid in the presence of a catalyst. Under these extreme conditions, the majority of any oxidizable material in the sample will be oxidized. As a consequence, C.O.D. values are normally greater than B.O.D.$_5$ values (often nearly double) and are more comparable with ultimate oxygen demands.

Potassium permanganate is also used as a chemical oxidant, usually at 27°C for 4 hours. Under these milder conditions, the permanganate value (P.V.) results are often comparable with B.O.D.$_5$ values. A field test version of the determination has been recommended particularly for monitoring effluents from small sewage works[3]. The visual appearance of the unreacted potassium permanganate after 30 minutes can be used to give a general classification of effluent quality.

The quicker chemical methods of analysis often show reasonable correlation with the more lengthy B.O.D.$_5$ test, especially for particular samples or types of samples. The chemical tests can be employed instead of the B.O.D.$_5$ test, provided that the correlation between the tests has been rigorously confirmed by experimental determination and is considered theoretically sound for the particular sample.

2.2.3   Instrumental methods

Several instrumental methods of determining the pollutional load from a sample are currently available.

The determination of total organic carbon (T.O.C.) relies upon combustion of the sample and measurement of the carbon dioxide produced from the carbon present in the sample. The determination of total oxygen demand (T.O.D.) involves combustion of the sample in an oxygen enriched gas stream at a platinum catalyst. The subsequent reduction in the concentration of oxygen in the gas stream is measured and interpreted as the amount of oxygen required to oxidize the sample fully − T.O.D.

Both measurements (T.O.C. and T.O.D.) can be related to the more conventional C.O.D. and B.O.D. parameters, especially for particular samples. The measurements, although rapid (15 min), are furthest removed from the biological processes which are likely to be employed to degrade the samples and are therefore measuring rather different parameters.

2.3   Solids determinations

While the determination of the oxygen demand of a sample indicates the proportion of the sample which is degradable and the amount of oxygen consumed in this process, it is also of value to understand the state and quantity of solid materials in the sample. These latter factors are particularly relevant to the design and operation of settlement tanks in a treatment process and to the control of discharges to receiving waters.

Evaporation and drying of a sample at approximately 105°C measures the total solids content of the sample[1]. Such a measure gives no selectivity. All solids, whether dissolved, floating, suspended or settled, are recorded. Usually it is more useful to record the suspended solids (S.S.) content by separating out the material which can be removed by settlement, centrifugation or filtration. A measure of the organic content can be obtained by combusting an evaporated sample at 600°C, usually in a muffle furnace; the loss on ignition is recorded as the volatile solids content. The volatile solids determination is usually interpreted as the organic and therefore degradable fraction of the sample.

2.4   Sludge quality

Various parameters have been developed to quantify the quality of sludges in activated sludge type treatment processes. It is usually necessary to ensure that a sludge settles reasonably quickly to give a clear supernatant liquor above the sludge, such that the subsequent settlement processes can provide an efficient separation. Tests are usually carried out over the convenient time period of 30 minutes, measuring the settled volume of sludge after 30 minutes and determining separately the initial suspended solids concentration of the activated sludge which is usually referred to as the mixed liquor suspended solids (M.L.S.S.). Two values have been derived from this data:

Sludge Volume Index S.V.I.

$$= \frac{\text{settled volume of sludge in 30 min (\%)}}{\text{M.L.S.S. (\%)}}$$

Sludge Density Index S.D.I.

$$= \frac{\text{M.L.S.S. (\%)} \times 100}{\text{settled volume of sludge in 30 min (\%)}}.$$

As these two concepts are similar, only the sludge volume index S.V.I. will be used subsequently. In general, a good sludge will have S.V.I. < 100 while a poor sludge will have S.V.I. > 200: e.g., an activated sludge of M.L.S.S. = 2000 mg/l = 0.2% solids. If, after 30 minutes, such a sludge settles to a volume of less than 20% of its initial volume, the S.V.I. < 100 and the general settlement characteristics of the sludge are likely to be good. Should the sludge develop a high M.L.S.S., e.g., 8000 mg/l which occurs particularly if a small activated sludge plant has not been desludged, even with an S.V.I. = 100 the sludge will only settle to 80% of its initial value after 30 minutes. The subsequent settlement of such a sludge is likely to be incomplete and the effluent poor.

A simplified version of this test, merely measuring the sludge volume after 30 minutes, is usually recommended for small works. This test is very simple and can therefore be carried out by untrained staff. The test should be performed at least once per day. The effectiveness of this procedure depends greatly upon the type of sludge and the control and supervision of the plant and operatives. In order to gain the maximum benefit from such results, it is necessary to have carried out some complete S.V.I. determinations especially during the first few months of routine working. A knowledge of the relationship between the settled volumes, S.V.I. and effluent quality for any given works is also essential to ensure efficient operation and maintenance. The results of the simple 30 minute settlement test are essential for diagnosing sudden changes in sludge characteristics and the need for desludging the plant.

2.5   Measurement of sludge properties

The sludges which are produced during sewage treatment processes are mainly water. There is considerable advantage in dewatering these sludges to facilitate the disposal of the sludges – Chapter 10. Two methods have been devised which estimate the ease of dewatering sludges. Detailed discussion of the experimental techniques and basic theory should be found in other texts[4] ; a brief outline is included to provide some basis, particularly for discussing the costing of dewatering and disposing of sludges.

The specific resistance (r) of a sludge is measured by filtering the sludge in a laboratory vacuum filtration apparatus. By measuring the volume of filtrate collected from the sample over a period of time and from a knowledge of the filter area, the applied pressure, the solids concentration of the sludge and the viscosity of the filtrate, the specific resistance can be calculated. The faster the water drains from the sludge, the easier a sludge will be to dewater and the lower will be the specific resistance (r) of the sludge. Sludges normally have a specific resistance of the order of 10^{13} m/kg; sludges with higher specific resistances will be more difficult to dewater.

The alternative method is to measure the capillary suction time (C.S.T.) of the sludge. A sample of sludge is placed on a piece of special absorbent paper. The water in the sludge will travel outward from the sludge. The time taken for the water to travel a standard distance is noted and recorded as the capillary suction time.

References

[1] *Analysis of Raw, Potable and Wastewaters*, Dept. of the Environment, H.M.S.O., London, 1972.

[2] *Chemistry for Sanitary Engineers*, C. L. Sawyer and P. L. McCarty, McGraw Hill, New York, 1967.

[3] *Operation and Management of Small Sewage Works*, Min. Housing and Local Government, H.M.S.O., London, 1965.

[4] *Principles of Water Quality Control*, T. H. Y. Tebbutt, Pergamon, Oxford, 1973.

3 Effluent discharge — legislation and standards

The maintenance of water quality is usually the responsibility of some national, regional or local administrative body. These authorities are responsible for ensuring that the water within their jurisdiction is of the requisite quality. Legislation has been enacted giving authorities the power to set and enforce standards which should be met by any discharge within their area. A community discharging sewage, usually to some surface water, stream, river or lake, is required to meet the standards imposed by the authority. The discharge standards imposed are usually those which can be met by standard treatment processes, e.g. biological treatment. The recommendations of the Royal Commission on Sewage Treatment (1912) are still widely accepted and usually serve as a general guideline for effluent standards. Local conditions affect the application of these standards to particular discharges. Therefore general discussion of discharge requirements can consider only averaged values.

The legal basis for effluent control will be considered for Scotland and for England and Wales. Camping and caravan sites are governed by additional legislation which relates primarily to the drainage and sanitation on the sites.

3.1 Legal responsibility for sewage treatment

The legal system in Britain is a mixture of common law and statute law. Common law consists of the rules and principles derived from the decisions of judges in cases. Statute law is the enactments of Parliament. Often Acts of Parliament are supplemented by administrative regulations made in accordance with the act. It is usually only through statute law that offences are created. In the field of water pollution the common law principles have proved an inadequate means of control. Parliament has therefore enacted statutes not only to reinforce common law principles but also to give legal powers to authorities to ensure that standards of water quality are maintained. The collection and treatment of sewage is covered by two types of statutory control: the Public Health Acts, which include clauses dealing with the drainage from dwellings, and the Rivers Acts which include clauses dealing with the treatment and discharge of sewage and effluents.

3.1.1 Common law

Common law gives a riparian owner the right to receive unpolluted water, to abstract water for ordinary purposes, and fishery and navigation rights.

The leading case at common law on water pollution control was an action in nuisance against a local authority who were shown to have permitted the building of houses without the associated sewage treatment facilities. This case established that the persons responsible for creating a development are responsible for ensuring adequate sewage treatment.

Because of the difficulties in proving a case of nuisance and because of an increased need, particularly in England, to use rivers as a source of drinking water, statutes have been enacted to control discharges more closely.

3.1.2   Public Health Acts

The drainage of premises in England and Wales is controlled by the Public Health Acts. The acts require public health authorities to provide and maintain public sewers to drain their district and to treat the sewage which is collected. Owners or occupiers of premises are entitled to connect their drains or sewers to the public sewer and to discharge domestic and surface water into the public sewer. The authorities can impose conditions as to the nature, composition and volume of the sewage and impose charges for receiving the sewage. Control of drainage in Scotland was previously less effective than in England and Wales. The Sewerage (Scotland) Act has made sewage control comparable to that in England and Wales.

For small communities with fluctuating populations this means that, if main drainage is available, it is usually easiest and cheapest to arrange direct discharge to a public sewer. In cases where this facility is not available, the drainage and treatment of the sewage has to be carried out by the owner of the premises.

3.1.3   Discharge of effluents

The control of discharges to English and Welsh rivers was governed by the Rivers (Prevention of Pollution) Acts 1951 and 1961 and was controlled by the river authorities set up under the Water Resources Act. The Rivers (Prevention of Pollution) Acts make it an offence for a person if he 'causes or knowingly permits to enter any stream any poisonous, noxious or polluting matter'. The two acts describe the powers of the authorities to set discharge standards for effluents, e.g. volume, point, composition, temperature, and to institute proceedings against possible offenders.

The relevant sections of the Public Health and Rivers Acts have been superseded in England and Wales by the Water Act 1973. This latter act combined all of the authorities concerned with aspects of water abstraction, supply and distribution, sewerage, sewage treatment and pollution prevention into ten water authorities. It is to the regional Water Authority that application is now made to discharge an effluent and it is this authority which sets and monitors discharge standards. The power of these authorities has been strengthened and extended by further statutes – Control of Pollution Act 1974.

Statutory power in Scotland was provided by the Rivers (Prevention of Pollution) (Scotland) Acts 1951 and 1965. The acts set up nine river purification boards in the south and west of the country and gave powers to the twelve local authorities in the more sparsely populated areas. The Local Government (Scotland) Act 1973 has redefined the areas under the jurisdiction of the river purification boards and has created a new board in the Highlands Area. In Scotland there are seven river purification boards and three island areas where control of discharges will be a function of the islands councils. In Scotland the supply of drinking water is controlled by separate authorities.

3.2 Camping and caravan sites
The discharges from camping and caravan sites clearly have to meet the specifications laid down by the relevant water authority or river board. Additionally, the use of the land is governed by the Town and Country Planning Acts, which necessitate planning permission for a new site.

The general layout of caravan sites is governed by the Caravan Sites and Control of Development Act 1960. The act empowers local authorities to license caravan sites. Models have been prepared, which sites are expected to follow in order to be licensed by the local authority. There are separate but similar Scottish and English models. The model sites have adequate sewerage systems and a chemical closet disposal point, sanitation at a toilet block is provided by 4 water closets (sometimes including urinals) and 2–4 wash basins for 15 caravans. For touring sites less stringent recommendations have been made: 3 water closets 1 urinal and 4 wash basins for 30 caravans.

Tented sites lack this separate control and currently lack national model standards. These sites are likely to be subject to similar standards to those imposed on the caravan sites but the standards are likely to be less stringent.

3.3 Discharge standards
The statutory bodies which control the discharge of effluents contain members who represent organisations which are likely to be polluters, e.g. local and regional councils. It is therefore unlikely that discharge standards will generally be imposed which cannot be reasonably fulfilled. The type of discharge standard which is usually required particularly specifies the volume, $B.O.D._5$ and suspended solids content of the effluent. Such standards were discussed in some detail in the Royal Commission on Sewage Disposal, although modification and extension of these guidelines has occurred.

3.3.1 Royal Commission standards
The Royal Commission on Sewage Disposal at the beginning of the century produced a series of reports dealing with several aspects of sewage treatment and disposal. Besides recommending the $B.O.D._5$ test as the major chemical assessment of water quality and pollution, they described river classifications and effluent discharge standards.

The report suggested a range of discharge standards for treated sewage effluents discharging in inland streams. The standards vary with the volume of clean diluting river water available in the receiving water. The commonly quoted standard, 30 mg/l suspended solids, 20 mg/l B.O.D.$_5$ was recommended for receiving water dilutions between 8 and 150. Such dilutions are commonly found in Britain and for domestic sewage the standard can be met by settlement followed by complete biological treatment.

For dilutions of less than 8, standards were not specifically defined and have usually been decided on a local basis. Typical requirements might be 10 mg/l B.O.D.$_5$ and 10 mg/l suspended solids, perhaps with some specification to ensure nitrification — control of ammonia or nitrate concentrations. Effluent standards can be met with a generously designed biological treatment plant which is well maintained and operated. For small sewage works the latter principles are rarely seen in practice. Some form of tertiary treatment is usually required to ensure that these more stringent standards are approached.

For receiving river water dilutions which lie between 150 and 500 the major effluent standard is that the suspended solids concentration should not exceed approximately 100 mg/l. Such a standard can be maintained by settlement or by settlement and partial biological treatment. For dilutions of greater than 500 in a clean river water, very little treatment is required. In order to maintain the aesthetic appearance of the river, it is usual to require screening and grit removal.

The Royal Commission also recommended that up to three times dry weather flow should be given full treatment and that 3–6 times dry weather flow should receive at least settlement in storm water tanks. These general guidelines are also commonly suggested in the design of treatment plants and effluent standards, although their relevance to small works is often more limited (see Chapters 4 and 15).

3.3.2 Anticipated discharge requirements

The Royal Commission made its recommendations over 50 years ago in conditions which differ from those of the present day. The lasting recommendations of the Commission indicate the general acceptance of the principles of their findings. The recommendations for discharge standards were intended to apply to clean river waters; the standards are likely to be modified if the river is already polluted. Standards are also varied to meet local conditions. A river which supports valuable fish — salmon, trout — requires water of a high quality, and is likely to have more stringent discharge standards than a similar river which has no recreational use. The maintenance of as high a quality of surface water as is financially viable is usually in the best interest of the owners. The attractions of small, isolated or holiday sites are greatly impaired by the loss of recreational potential due to man-made water pollution.

The suggested full treatment of 3 times dry weather flow and partial treatment of 3–6 times dry weather flow is also more flexible at certain sites. The choice of drainage system, the annual total rainfall, monthly rainfall distribution, hydraulic predictions and sewer structure can all alter treatment requirements: e.g., a hotel with a separate water-tight sewerage system should be able to predict accurately the flow to the sewage works, is not likely to require storm water capacity and should be able to provide effective treatment with less than 3 times dry weather flow capacity. A small community with a combined sewerage system may require full treatment for between 3 and 9 times dry weather flow.

The increased demands for water and for recreational use of water have suggested that effluent standards will become stricter. Particularly standards which are aimed purely at sewage settlement or septic tank installations (80–160 mg/l suspended solids) are likely to be tightened to necessitate full biological treatment. Increased flows from existing sites are also likely to require more complete treatment, either full biological treatment or full biological treatment and tertiary treatment. The recent additional legislation should ensure the enforcement of effluent standards.

Suggested further reading

[1] *River Pollution 3: Control*, L. Klein, Butterworths, London, 1966.
[2] *The Law Relating to Pollution*, J. McLoughlin, Manchester Univ. Press, Manchester, 1972.

4 Difficulties of sewage treatment at small and variable communities

The types of communities considered in this book have certain inherent characteristics which make the treatment of sewage more difficult than for larger communities. These difficulties are usually related to the small size of the community, the restricted positions available for the sewage works, or the varied and fluctuating sewage loads which are generated by the community. Often similar problems are encountered at larger works, but the size and nature of the smaller communities exaggerate these difficulties, such that they can seriously affect treatment plant design and performance. Prediction of the hydraulic and B.O.D. loading on small plants is often uncertain. These factors, together with poor operation and maintenance, often account for the poor performance of small treatment plants.

4.1 Flow and loading factors for sewage works design

For the design and operation of all treatment plants, an accurate knowledge of the sewage flow and sewage characteristics is essential. The daily volume of sewage per capita can vary from less than 50 l for a relatively primitive camping site to more than 300 l for an affluent high amenity residential area. Similarly, the strength of sewage in an area drained by a sewerage system which permits the inclusion of surface water can be low, with a $B.O.D._5$ of less than 100 mg/l, while the wastes from chemical closets can have a $B.O.D._5$ in excess of 10 000 mg/l.

In order to accurately determine the flow and $B.O.D._5$ of a particular sewage, the best method is to measure both parameters over a representative time period. If this procedure cannot be followed, some less rigorous method has to be adopted. Comparison with a similar site is advantageous, modifying the data in the light of particular circumstances. Often designs are based almost entirely upon educated estimates of flows and $B.O.D._5$ values. Even for cases when estimates are used, it is important to critically assess these design parameters.

4.1.1 Mass of $B.O.D._5$

The figures for per capita flow and per capita $B.O.D._5$ can be combined to express a total per capita mass of $B.O.D._5$ which will require treatment. For a daily average per capita flow of 135 l (30 gal) and an average per capita B.O.D.$_5$ of 400 mg/l.

$$\text{Daily per capita B.O.D.}_5 = \frac{135 \times 400}{10^6}$$

$$= 0.054 \text{ kg } (0.12 \text{ lb}).$$

A similar result would be obtained from a per capita B.O.D.$_5$ of 1000 mg/l and a per capita flow of 54 l or a B.O.D.$_5$ of 100 mg/l and a flow of 540 l. While the per capita flow of sewage tends to vary, the actual mass of B.O.D.$_5$ per capita for domestic sewages is often between 0.04 and 0.07 kg/d.

4.1.2   Dry weather flow (D.W.F.)
The daily measured flow at a sewage works during a period of dry weather is referred to as the dry weather flow (D.W.F.). In the absence of flow measurements, the D.W.F. is computed from the product of population and per capita sewage flow or water consumption. For a community of 100 persons with an average per capita sewage flow of 200 l/d:

$$\text{Dry Weather Flow} = 200 \times 100 \text{ l}$$
$$= 20\,000 \text{ l}$$
$$= 20 \text{ m}^3.$$

This represents a flow of 20 000 l/24 hours, or 833.3 l/h or 13.8 l/min or 0.23 l/s. At a large sewage works the flows entering the works in dry weather are likely to be ±50% of the D.W.F. at any point in time. While for small communities much more erratic flow patterns are observed and flows well in excess of the D.W.F. are common, the usefulness of D.W.F. as a concept in the design of small works is more limited. Besides a consideration of D.W.F., it is therefore instructive to consider peak flows and the variations of sewage flow during a day and during a year.

4.2   Diurnal variations in sewage flows and treatment capacity
One of the major factors which influence the characteristics and volumes of sewage is the nature of the drainage system. A completely separate sewerage system only includes foul sewage in the foul sewer for treatment at the sewage works. A combined sewerage system includes foul sewage and surface waters within the one sewer. A range of intermediate conditions can exist with varying volumes of surface water entering the foul sewer. It is useful to consider the variations in flow and the implications for maximum treatment volumes of the two types of sewerage system.

4.2.1   Separate sewerage systems
The pattern of sewage flows during the course of any day is usually similar for all communities – minimum flow at night, maximum flows in the morning and

evening. For small communities, this pattern of diurnal flow is usually more extreme than for larger communities. Diurnal flow variation is best illustrated for a system which is compact and has no infiltration of surface water. Data collected on water usage in blocks of flats[1] gives the best illustration of the daily flow changes (Fig. 4.1). Flows during the night are minimal but increase sharply after 6.00 hours to give a maximum flow between 8.00 and 9.00 hours; smaller but significant peak flows are observed between 12.00 and 13.00, 17.00 and 18.00, and 22.00 and 23.00 hours.

Small communities of any type are likely to show the wide variations of flow illustrated in Fig. 4.1. The short sewer lengths can provide little flow balancing, so high peak flows can be expected. It is not uncommon for peak flows to far exceed average D.W.F.'s. During the early morning peak flow, much of the flow is from water closets. For a community which contains 100 water closets, it is most likely that 4 will be flushed simultaneously[2] and the instantaneous flow would be 17 D.W.F. The actual flow to a sewage works is likely to be less, but the most likely flow would still be near or above 3 D.W.F. Flows in excess of 3 D.W.F. for short time periods are, therefore, highly likely from a small separate sewerage system.

The incidence of these hydraulic peaks makes the specification of flow splitting at 3 D.W.F. less logical for small communities. There is a high statistical chance that undiluted foul sewage would be discharged or receive only partial treatment, if only 3 D.W.F. were passed for full treatment. CP 302: 1972, which describes the general design of small sewage works[3], specifies that only foul sewage should be treated, and makes no recommendation for overflows prior to

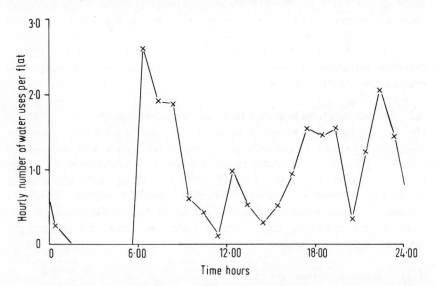

4.1   Diurnal water uses from a multi-storey block of flats (Crown copyright. Reproduced by permission of the Director, Building Research Establishment).

the works. The recommended design criteria[3] incorporate over capacity as a necessary precaution to alleviate the difficulties of short duration peak flows. These peak flows make the provision of flow balancing devices a serious proposition, particularly for small communities which are likely to experience extreme flow variations – see Sections 4.6, 4.7 and 4.8.

4.2.2 Combined sewerage systems

The inclusion of surface or storm waters with foul sewage will result in high sewage flows at times of high rainfall. The magnitude of this flow will depend upon the design and state of repair of the sewerage system, and the area and nature of the surfaces drained. Flows well in excess of 3 D.W.F. are highly probable during periods of rainfall; these flows can therefore be for prolonged periods. Complete treatment for the entire flows under storm conditions is neither desirable nor practical at a small works. Prolonged high hydraulic sewage flows will cause the failure of biological treatment plants, particularly the 'wash out' of materials from the final settlement stage. Simple geometric increase in the capacity of the plant will seriously underload the units under normal flow conditions.

It is usual to make some provision for the separate discharge or partial treatment of storm flows. The inclusion of a storm water tank to take flows in excess of 3 D.W.F. is not usually favoured at small works. The additional labour, maintenance and difficulties involved in storm tank management are usually prohibitive. Instead, overflow weirs are set to discharge storm sewages with minimum treatment, once excessive flows are experienced. The recommendations for storm water overflows for domestic sewage[4] suggest that flows in excess of approximately 7.5 D.W.F. can be discharged directly. The actual figure set usually takes account of local factors, for example, receiving water flows and quality, storm frequency and duration, and is usually a point for discussion with the statutory authority. The design of the sewage treatment units cannot be made on the basis of CP 302: 1972[3] and some adjustment, particularly of the final settlement capacities, is advisable.

4.3 Annual variations in sewage flows

In Britain, the flow of sewage from a constant population shows little variation throughout the year. Certain communities, however, have a very variable population. Such communities are usually associated with some seasonal activity which results in an influx of visitors for certain periods of the year. It is usual to design sewage treatment plants to accommodate the maximum flow of sewage and to make provision for treatment at times of low flows.

The degree of variability differs for different types of community. Small permanent villages which cater for some holiday traffic will show least variation and can usually be predicted easily. Camping and caravan sites show much greater variations, while more permanent facilities – chalets, hotels – present problems of intermediate complexity.

In the U.K. it is common practice to close camping and caravan sites on, or about, October 1st, and to open on, or about, Easter. The site is likely to be full or overflowing during the school holidays (July and August) and to be partially filled for the remaining period of time (April, May, June, September) (Tables 4.1 and 4.2). The actual occupancy varies for different types of site and with the location of the site. The summer holiday season in Scotland is very short[5] (Tables 4.1, 4.2) where the climate limits tourists to only three months, while a more extended peak season would be expected for sites in southern England.

During the periods of only partial occupancy, sites tend to be subject to very variable demands. At holiday periods, even out of the school summer holidays, e.g. Easter, Spring, 'Bank' holiday, fine weekends, sites can be 100% full, while the following workday, sites are likely to be reduced to perhaps 10% capacity. The general yearly pattern of occupancy is therefore the site opening to receive a few permanent staff just prior to Easter, to be followed by a short period of high occupancy (50–100%) which decreases the following week to a small population (5–20% occupancy). Between April and the end of June, the average occupancy figures rise steadily from about 10% to 60%. During this period, climate and

Table 4.1   *Total number of camper nights at the 100 pitch camp site at Rowardennan*

Month	Total camper nights
April	2724
May	3399
June	5739
July	9146
August	11991
September	4616

Published by courtesy of the Forestry Commission.

Table 4.2   *Touring caravan holidays in Scotland (1970)*

Total of	102 000 caravan holidays
	369 000 caravanners
Average	3.6 persons/caravan

Month	% of Total caravanners
June	9.2
July	14.2
August	41.9
September	26.9
Rest	7.8

Published by courtesy of the Scottish Tourist Board[5].

local factors produce erratic fluctuations in populations which can include 100% and 10% occupancy on successive days. During July and August, the sites are usually at least 90% full, while during September occupancy figures fall from 90% to nearer 20% full. Sites are usually closed to visitors in early October and may or may not have a small number of residents during the winter months. Sites are therefore likely to be effectively full for about 3 months, have moderate occupancy for 1−2 months, and very variable occupancy for 1−2 months.

Such a pattern of occupancy will generate a flow of sewage which imposes very serious constraints upon sewage treatment facilities. The treatment works need to be large enough to withstand shock loads and to treat the flows during maximum occupancy. The works need to be small enough to avoid problems of underfeeding micro-organisms and the associated poor sludge characteristics and poor quality effluents for low loading rates. The works also need to be able to 'start up' very quickly to accommodate the large populations which can occur at the beginning of the season, and flexible enough to adjust to the often wide variations of flow which often occur, and be capable of completely closing down or functioning on very low loads (see Section 14.11). Such restrictions are almost prohibitive and cannot be easily met by a single unit treatment plant. In order to begin to meet these types of specifications, it is usually necessary to have some sub-division of the sewage works. Provision of a duplicate system with a total capacity equal to the design size can be advantageous. If it is not economically feasible to split the plant completely, provision of twin\ aerobic biological units each of 50% design capacity and full scale settlement units is often the best alternative. One of the biological units will work continuously while the other will only come into operation once the sewage flows exceed 50% of the total designed flow. With very large sites, further subdivision is highly desirable.

4.4 Origin and characteristics of sewage

In the absence of analytical data, it is often necessary to estimate loading factors. In order to make reliable estimates, it is useful to consider the components of domestic sewage and their contribution to sewage flows, S.S. and B.O.D.$_5$ values.

Water closets and washing facilities (basins and baths) usually each constitute approximately one third of the total volume of sewage; the characteristics of these major components are very different (Table 4.3). These general figures, although based upon American data[6], indicate the relative importance of the various processes. In normal use, the major S.S. and B.O.D.$_5$ contributions are from the water closet (approximately 50%) and to a large extent the majority of this sewage is flushing water. For normal domestic sewage, the per capita values of B.O.D.$_5$/d and S.S./d are similar. The inclusion of wastes from garbage grinders significantly increases the B.O.D.$_5$ and S.S. value of the sewage (Table 4.3), B.O.D.$_5$ of sewage per capita increases from 0.05 kg/d without garbage

Table 4.3   *Daily sewage characteristics for a community of four persons*

Source	Uses/d	Volume l/use	Total Volume l	B.O.D.$_5$ g/d	S.S. g/d
Toilet	16	20	320	94.2	126.0
Bath/Shower	2	100	200	35.4	22.6
Laundry	1	150	150	38.5	29.5
Dishwashing	2	30	60	23.6	11.8
Totals			730	191.7	189.9
Total/cap.			182.5	47.9	47.5
Garbage disposal	3	8	24	126.0	174.0
Totals including					
Garbage disposal			754	317.7	363.9
Total/cap. including					
Garbage disposal			188.5	79.4	91.0

Published by courtesy of the American Society of Civil Engineers[6].

grinders to 0.08 kg/d with garbage grinders[6]. There is only a very small increase in the hydraulic load to a plant on the installation of garbage grinders. The increased pollutional load to a sewage works must be taken into account. It is usually prudent to allow for at least an additional 50% B.O.D. and S.S. load to the works above normal domestic figures. If garbage grinders are installed only in a proportion of the dwellings, suitable proportional adjustments in load are required.

Garbage grinders encourage the water borne disposal of a range of materials which are non biodegradable or are unsuitable for disposal to a sewage works, e.g. milk bottle tops, paper, plastic. In certain cases these materials can have a serious deleterious effect upon the performance of a works. Such effects are particularly noticeable at established works when garbage grinders are installed into existing dwellings. Even the installation of a small number of garbage grinders have been known to affect adversely the performance of small\sewage works. The increased suspended solids load to sewers can cause increased silting in sewerage systems which have poor flow characteristics. It is therefore clear that, while adjustments of design criteria can be made to accommodate the wastes from garbage grinders, their installation should be discouraged. The additional burden at a sewage works can have little justification when separate garbage/refuse collection is available.

4.5   Small communities
In order to obtain accurate estimates of the flow and loads of sewage from a small community, in the absence of analytical data, figures for population, per capita flow and per capita B.O.D.$_5$ are usually required.

4.5.1   Population
The total population of a community can usually be obtained accurately from census data. Changes of population over short time periods (5 years) can often

be accurately gauged from a knowledge of planning permission applications or grants. If estimates are made solely from the number of dwellings, it is important to make reasonable estimates of likely rates of occupancy. The average number of persons per house has fallen in Britain over the last fifty years from approximately 4.5 persons per house to less than 3 persons per house. Significant modifications are needed to account for typical sites. Multi-occupancy can result in very large and variable numbers of persons per dwelling, while specialized housing — old people's bungalows, small flats — will have a low rate of occupancy, often less than 2 persons per dwelling.

At static communities, these figures should remain sensibly constant throughout the year. Modifications to account for significant seasonal fluctuations can usually be made from a knowledge of the availability of local accommodation.

4.5.2 Per capita sewage flow

It is usually reported that the per capita flow of sewage from small communities is less than from larger communities. This partially reflects the significant industrial demands for water which are more common for larger communities. However, previously even domestic sewage flows per capita were smaller in villages (<100 l/d) than in towns (~200 l/d). More widespread installation of piped water supplies, together with generally increased living standards which are accompanied by increased water consumption — washing machines, car washing — have eliminated many of the differences in water demand and sewage flow. However, there are reports of small communities which still have low demands for water. The best initial estimate of per capita sewage flow is usually the average domestic flow in the area. This accounts for regional (or national) differences, and can be further modified to suit individual communities. Modern developments for middle or higher income groups can be expected to generate sewage flows above the regional average. Per capita sewage flows of 200–250 l/d are often applicable to high amenity areas, while normally per capita flows between 120 and 180 l/d are quoted for the design of plants for small communities.

Usually, the diurnal flow pattern (Section 4.2) is not sufficiently extreme to cause major problems in the treatment of sewage, as these factors are accounted for in the design criteria[3]. These fluctuations in flow at certain small communities can be further exaggerated by local employment patterns. It is not uncommon for there to be one dominant employer in a small community. The imposition of the working timetable upon the patterns of food preparation and water closet use can cause greater variations in sewage flow. In very extreme cases, some form of flow balancing may be advantageous.

4.5.3 Per capita B.O.D.$_5$ values

The major contributing factor to the B.O.D.$_5$ (and S.S.) value of domestic sewage is from the water closet (Table 4.3). This B.O.D.$_5$ contribution is therefore likely to be similar for all types of community. Differences are likely to be the result of greater water use which will produce more sewage of weaker strength. More affluent communities use more water and produce larger volumes of weaker sewage. These greater flows are caused particularly by the greater use of automatic labour-saving, water-utilizing devices, e.g. dish-washers, automatic washing machines. In the case of washing machines, for similar dry weights of washing, top loading automatic machines (~120 l) use larger volumes of water than are required for front loading machines, which in turn require almost twice the volume used by twin tubs and traditional machines (25–55 l). The widespread household use of front loading automatic washing machines will therefore increase the sewage flow by up to 15% without significantly altering the total B.O.D.$_5$ value. Automatic dish-washing machines, although not yet common in the U.K., have a similar effect upon sewage characteristics. Thus in higher income communities, sewage flows would be expected to be at least 25% higher than from lower income communities, and the difference can reach 100%. The B.O.D.$_5$ of the sewage will show an inverse relationship with these flow figures. Greater per capita volumes of sewage are usually of weaker strength. The mass of B.O.D.$_5$ for most communities is therefore likely to be more constant; per capita figures between 0.04 and 0.07 kg/d are usual, and design per capita figures of 0.05 and 0.055 kg/d are common. Garbage grinders will seriously distort these figures (Section 4.4) and should be accounted for.

4.6.   Camping and caravan sites

4.6.1   Population
Predictions of populations and population changes at seasonal camping and caravan sites often present a major problem. The factors described in Section 4.3 are applicable to most seasonal sites. The fluctuating populations usually represent an operational problem rather than a design problem. Provided that the site expects full occupancy for a significant period, the figures for full occupancy can be used in computing design figures. Plants should then be chosen and designed to give operational flexibility.

If not accurately measurable, the number of persons at a site usually has to be computed from the number of pitches and an average rate of occupancy. If accurate average occupancy figures are available, this data is clearly useful; e.g., for touring caravans in Scotland, the average number of persons per caravan is 3.6 (Table 4.2). Local estimation of the actual number of persons per tent or caravan is often required to account for the predicted clientele of a particular site – usually figures of between 2.2 and 3.7 persons per caravan are likely.

4.6.2   Flow and B.O.D.$_5$ loadings
The actual flow or loading at a given site is very dependent upon the nature of the site. Camping and caravan sites vary from minimum facility sites to very sophisticated sites complete with hot and cold water supplies, wash basins, showers, laundry facilities, flush toilets, shop and restaurant facilities. As a first

approximation, the volumes of sewage produced at a given site can be estimated on the basis of a five star system. The basic site outlined above would be a one star site, the sophisticated site a five star site. Sewage flows can then be computed on a daily per capita basis at 40–50 l/star. As a useful guide, modern reasonable sites in Britain can often be assessed at about 60% of the hydraulic and $B.O.D._5$ load for an equivalent fixed community. Such a classification can only act as an initial estimate and requires modification in the light of the facilities available and their usage. Similarly, the total $B.O.D._5$ for a five star site is likely to be similar on a per capita basis to that of a small community, 0.05–0.06 kg/d. However, a basic site (one star) will not have such a decrease in $B.O.D._5$ values. As the major contribution to $B.O.D._5$ is from the water closet and urinals (Table 4.3) provided that these facilities are fully utilised (see below). $B.O.D._5$ values cannot fall below 0.02 kg/d for each person.

The sewage characteristics at a camping and caravan site are also influenced by the degree of use which the facilities receive. Again, generalizations are difficult but a useful guide is the predominant length of stay and type of tourist who visits the site, which are often functions of the locations of sites and their distances from centres of interest. The sites can be classified for the purposes of sewage into three types: stopover, touring and semi-residential. Stopover sites will have a high turnover of tourists with low average residence times (1 or 2 nights). Such sites serve mainly as transit points or are near to places of marginal interest to tourists. These sites are less common in Britain. The flow and load of sewage generated will be shortened into two periods, early evening and early morning, and total amounts will be less than for a given quality of site, perhaps reduced by a third.

Touring sites are likely to have longer occupancy times and would be expected to act as centres for a holiday. However, the attraction of the area – beach, mountains, historic interests – is distant from the site and the occupants would be expected to spend a large proportion of the daylight hours outside of the camp site. Such a site will have similar sewage patterns and characteristics to a stopover site but is usually a higher quality of site. Semi-residential sites would expect the residents to spend the majority of their time at the site. This is likely to occur particularly if the site is near to the central attraction – often a beach – or provides sufficient attractions to become a holiday centre in its own right. This latter type of site would be expected to have a similar volume and type of sewage to an equivalent small community. The nature of these sites usually necessitates the provision of adequate facilities so that they are usually better quality sites.

The actual $B.O.D._5$ loading factors are often critically dependent upon the use of toilet facilities and particularly at camping and caravan sites, the use of these facilities can be very significant in determining actual loadings (Table 4.3). These considerations are of direct relevance at sites which are not fully occupied all day, and at sites which contain significant numbers of caravans equipped with chemical closets (>15% of pitches). While a more detailed discussion of chemical sanitation is postponed until Chapter 5, a brief mention is warranted. Modern sanitary fluids for caravans in the U.K. rely upon formaldehyde to sterilize wastes from water closets. The contents of chemical sanitation units, therefore, contain wastes diluted with a minimum of water and have a high B.O.D. and solids content. The $B.O.D._5$ of such solutions is usually near 10 000 mg/l and contains chemical additives which are potentially toxic to biological sewage treatment plants. Chemically treated sewages are usually disposed of separately or can be added in a controlled manner to a sewage works. If the wastes are disposed of separately (burying or tankering), the remaining water borne sewage will have a lower total $B.O.D._5$, reduced by perhaps 50% to 0.02–0.04 kg/d for each person. The volume of sewage is reduced by a similar factor (50%) because of the non-use of flush toilets, but the strength of the remaining sewage flow will be similar to that of normal domestic sewage (250–450 mg/l). If the wastes are mixed with the water borne sewage, the flow of sewage will still be greatly reduced (by 40–50%) but the average strength will be greater (double) such that the total $B.O.D._5$ is similar to that of normal domestic sewage. The provision of adequate arrangements for the disposal of the liquids from chemical sanitation units and the prevention of shock overloads require careful consideration, and are discussed in more detail in Chapter 5.

At camping and caravan sites it is therefore vitally important to make an accurate assessment of the flow and strength of sewage. This involves a consideration of the likely yearly variation in occupancy, the facilities provided, use of the facilities, likely residence times, patterns of behaviour of residents, use of chemical sanitation units and the disposal of liquids from chemical sanitation units. Even after detailed consideration, it is rarely possible to be certain of design criteria, and for many locations per capita figures of approximately 100–180 l/d and 0.045 kg of $B.O.D._5$/d are useful. The variations of flow and|the possibility of the discharge of liquids from chemical sanitation units make the effective control of the site and operation of the sewage works of great importance at camping and caravan centres.

4.7 Hotels

4.7.1 Population

Hotels are subject to certain of the restrictions imposed by the annual population changes described previously for camping and caravan sites. Usually these changes are less severe. Hotels tend to have larger permanent staffs than camping and caravan sites and are less likely to close completely during the winter months. While some seasonal changes in the total number of occupants is to be expected, extremes are rare, and the number of occupants less dependent upon climate and usually more predictable. Predictions may be required to account for the use of non residential facilities – bar and dining room.

4.7.2 Flow and $B.O.D._5$ loadings

A fully residential hotel will have similar or larger per capita sewage flows and loadings than small fixed communities. The loads from catering and from non residential patronage often warrant separate consideration. Hotel catering varies from heating pre-cooked meals to the complete preparation of meals. The former should impose little additional demand upon a sewage works, but the latter can create additional flows of water borne sewage. Hotel and canteen catering tends to produce proportionally more sewage than domestic food preparation (Table 4.3). Flows of 10–15 l/meal and $B.O.D._5$ loads of 0.01–0.02 kg/meal are often used. The influence of a bar trade can also be unpredictable; estimates of liquid sold, automatic urinal flushing and water closet use can be taken into account. Per capita flows of 5–15 l and 0.003–0.01 kg $B.O.D._5$ can usually be assumed. The inclusion of garbage grinders at hotels encourages the disposal of more materials to the sewers. While flows would only increase slightly (<20%), $B.O.D._5$, loads can double (Table 4.3). In extreme cases, the imposition of this additional flow upon the overall diurnal pattern can cause high peak flows which may necessitate flow balancing.

The nature of hotel catering often results in a higher fat content than would be expected from normal domestic sewage. The presence of excess fat in aerobic treatment plants can block pipes and weirs, and form unsightly noxious scum and fat balls on the surface of the treatment plants. Fat traps are available and should be adequately installed and maintained.

A range of chemical cleaning and sterilising reagents is used in kitchens, bathrooms and water closets. In domestic use they rarely create problems; it is statistically unlikely that a sufficiently high proportion of the population will simultaneously discharge bactericidal solutions to the sewers. However, in hotels the cleaning of domestic and sanitary appliances is more regimented and often occurs at times of low sewage flow. The organized cleaning and short sewer lengths can therefore combine to produce relatively strong solutions in sewage of proprietary chemicals advertised as bactericides. These materials can inhibit the microbiological action necessary at a biological sewage treatment plant. If such an effect is suspected, attempts should be made to restrict or stagger the use of such chemicals.

Wastes from laundries at hotels provide a similar example. Large volumes of water are generated by commercial washing processes and significant shock hydraulic loads may occur. It is important that allowances are made for these operations if they are to be installed in a hotel. Laundry wastes usually include significant quantities of commercial detergent. The presence of such detergents is not normally adverse but, as a shock load, can disrupt microbiological action. Attention should be given to these effects if hydraulic wash out or poisoning of biomass is suspected.

4.8 Other types of community

A range of sites not connected to main drainage exists and requires sewage treatment facilities. Such sites would include schools, hospitals, offices, public houses; the loads from these establishments are likely to be different to those from small communities. Non-residential sites – offices, schools, sports grounds, are likely to have much lower loads, with the total hydraulic flow and $B.O.D._5$

load reduced to between 20 and 40% of that from a small community, e.g. per capita figures of 50 l/d and 0.02 kg/d. Public houses are likely to have a small fixed residential population plus the imposition of high flows from the bar trade as in Section 4.7.

The nature of toilet and washing facilities and the limited periods of time available for their use increases the frequency[2] of use of the facilities during certain periods of a day. Peak flows can therefore be very large and, as the per capita design figure is likely to be small (50 l/d), peak flows in excess of 6 D.W.F. can be expected. Sites of limited occupancy are those which are most likely to require some form of flow balancing.

Certain types of site, e.g. hospitals, will produce high flows of highly polluting liquid – per capita flows from a hospital can exceed 400 l/d with B.O.D.$_5$ values in excess of 0.1 kg/d. Specialist examples of this type require more specialist advice. Similarly, the treatment of industrial wastes is beyond the scope of this book; however, effluents from industrial processes are discharged to the sewers even in small communities. A range of industrial and agricultural wastes is discharged to sewers. It is usual to classify these wastes by their B.O.D.$_5$ and S.S., although additional data may be required for particular wastewaters. If such a wastewater is expected to constitute an important proportion of the sewage flow, or to be particularly difficult to treat, again more specialist advice should be sought.

4.9   Problems associated with the siting of a sewage works

The positions available for small sewage works are often limited by local topography, the cost of sewerage and aesthetic considerations. Positions may therefore have to be used which would not normally be considered suitable.

The presence of deciduous trees creates the problem of falling leaves which can block pipes, air lifts, weirs, filters and screens. The leaves need to be removed regularly or the works protected by mesh covers. Roots from large trees disrupt engineering structures and can lead to the fracture of buried tanks and pipes.

Exposed sites are more prone to freezing in winter than protected sites. While flowing sewage is unlikely to freeze, static or impeded sewage, e.g. in the dosing chamber of a percolating filter or at a screen, is prone to freezing and may require the construction of a wind break or covering. It is normal practice to cover rotating disc units partly to avoid freezing.

At sites which have little natural gradient or are unsuitable for the construction of a complete sewerage system due to difficult topography, some form of sewage pumping may be necessary. The design basis for pumping stations is given in other texts[7]. The most relevant factor in sewage treatment is the addition of the sewage to the works. In pumping from a sump, if the capacity of the sump is too large, the sewage can turn anaerobic during low flows; if too small, the sump can overflow or the pump operate too frequently. The pumping of large volumes of sewage into a small works is also likely to cause incomplete treatment and hydraulic wash out of biological materials.

All structures sited on soil as opposed to rock are liable to differential settlement, while buried structures are additionally subject to flotation. In extreme cases these effects can cause the fracture of connecting pipework, but even slight tilting of a small works can cause uneven flows over weirs and distort predicted overflow rates. It is therefore critical particularly during the commissioning of works, to keep buried tanks filled with water or sewage, to prevent flotation. A knowledge of the water table and of possible compaction of underlying soils is therefore extremely useful and at certain sites essential. These problems are often more extreme for small works than for larger works. Periodic rather than automatic continuous desludging often means that tanks have to be completely emptied during desludging. Care should be taken to minimize flotation during these processes. The works are often installed by workers inexperienced in the implications of flotation. At such sites, experienced supervision is required. For plants made from lighter weight constructional materials, e.g. fibreglass, these difficulties are likely to be more extreme than for heavier materials (concrete). For particularly difficult sites, plants can be positioned above ground level or only partly buried. These options are sometimes restricted by the aesthetic appearance or acceptance of the sewage treatment works.

Units manufactured from steel are liable to corrosion. Most manufacturers supply the units treated with a protective paint or suggest suitable paints. These paints include epoxy, bitumastic and chlorinated rubber products, and usually ensure adequate protection. The most likely points of corrosion on water holding steel tanks are at the liquid-air interface inside the tank, and the soil-air interface outside the tank. Certain manufacturers recommend or supply different paints for the two levels to minimize corrosion at the interface. For soil conditions which are known to be particularly aggressive, cathodic protection can be installed. Specialist advice may be required if aggressive soils are suspected, and package plant manufacturers can usually supply the appropriate equipment.

4.10 Miscellaneous problems

A range of problems has been reported during the installation and operation of small works. Many of these are of localized importance; the presence of large solid materials in sewage and of power failure are of more general interest.

The presence of large solid materials in sewage often presents greater problems than at large works. Grit channels are less common, so there is a tendency to accumulate grit in the aeration tank of a works which does not have primary settlement. The discharge of non-biodegradable materials (plastic, metal) or only slowly degraded materials (paper, clothes) can cause blockage of weirs, pipes, filters and screens. The tendency towards the production of articles classed as disposable which are non re-usable rather than degradable, has produced a larger amount of these materials in sewage. 'Disposable' nappies are reported to be often responsible for blocking the inlet to septic tanks, and can cause similar problems at other types of works. The discharge of these materials to the sewers should be discouraged, particularly for materials which can cause blockages and are known to be non degradable at sewage works, and for which normal refuse/garbage collection is adequate, e.g. rags and proprietary cleaning cloths.

Failure of the electricity supply to a small sewage works clearly creates significant short term difficulties. Treatment processes which rely heavily upon external power, such as activated sludge and the rotating biological filter, can provide little biological treatment during periods of electricity supply failure. The restarting of plants after short periods of failure is usually straightforward. Restarting a rotating disc plant, particularly a partially dehydrated system, is more likely to produce mechanical failure.

While failure of mechanical and electrical components is unavoidable, whenever possible standby equipment should be available to facilitate maintenance and to minimize stoppages. For example, extra compressor capacity should always be installed at diffused air activated sludge plants; the usual policy is to provide one or two working and one standby unit, and to rotate the operation of the machines.

4.11   Operation and maintenance

The importance of effective operation procedures and continued maintenance of a small sewage works is vital for the production of a good quality effluent. While considerable capital expense is often incurred in the provision of a sewage works – £5000–£20 000 is common – operation and maintenance are often neglected. Plants often receive only erratic visits, usually by persons with no knowledge or training in the theory or practice of sewage treatment. Sewage works are made the responsibility of a gardener (because it is in the grounds), a handyman (because their work often involves some mechanical expertise), a hotel manager (because the entire hotel is his responsibility), a camping or caravan site warden or manager – who may be a full-time permanent resident or part-time and normally a student, retired bank manager, retired salesman or a member of any profession except one relevant to public health engineering.

Most plants need at least daily inspection and maintenance (see Chapter 14). It is therefore imperative that the plant operator is given detailed instructions as to his duties and that a copy of any instruction manual is readily available to him and not merely to the plant purchaser.

4.12   Conclusions

For small sewage works, two of the most important factors are the accurate assessment of the loads which will require treatment and the operation of the plant once installed. The accurate prediction or measurement of hydraulic and pollutional load to be received by the works is essential for the design of a works. Once the design has been formulated, the plant constructed and operated successfully, major changes should not be made in the volume or nature of the sewage. While some tolerance is normally common (±10%) and larger variations (±30%) can be accommodated with careful operation, major changes will cause serious failure. The connection of storm water runoff to a system designed to accommodate only foul water is likely to cause a 'wash out' of biomass and poor quality effluents. Fig. 4.2 illustrates the effect of a sharply increased sewage flow on the S.S. of effluent from a small activated sludge package plant. The suspended solids content of the effluent rises rapidly after the hydraulic increase and contains a high concentration of activated sludge floc. The subsequent M.L.S.S. of the aeration tank is too low and subsequent sewage receives inadequate biological treatment. The avoidance of shock hydraulic loads is therefore particularly important, and flow balancing and separate aerobic digestion should be encouraged.

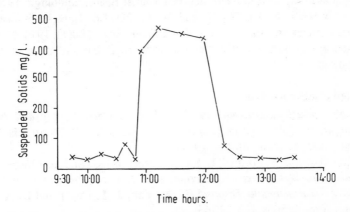

4.2   Influence of a shock hydraulic sewage flow on the suspended solids content of final effluent from a small extended aeration package plant.

Attention to the operation and maintenance of a well designed sewage works is equally essential to ensure a good effluent. Regular cleaning of weirs and equipment servicing must be carried out. All effective sewage treatment works accumulate sludge; this sludge must be removed at convenient intervals to ensure continued operation of the plant. Failure to carry out desludging is a major cause of poor treatment at small sewage works. More detailed guidelines about desludging are given in Chapters 7, 10 and 14.

While it is possible to indicate certain of the more common problems associated with the design and operation of small sewage works, few general statements can be provided. Instead, as accurate an assessment as possible of the likely loads must be made often in the absence of reliable data. Consideration of the character and background of the community served is usually a useful step in the estimation of sewage flows and strengths. The composition of the sewage should, if possible, be maintained constant and the plant operated by competent operators.

References

[1] C. J. D. WEBSTER, An investigation of the use of water outlets in multi-storey flats, *Building Services Engineer*, **39**, 1972, 215–233.

[2] C. J. HARTLEY, Calculation of foul sewage flows in small sewerage schemes and building drainage systems, *J. Inst. Publ. Health Eng.*, **67**, 1968, 233–243.

[3] British Standard Code of Practice CP 302: 1972, *Small Sewage Treatment Works*, British Standards Institution, London, 1972.

[4] *Technical Committee on Storm Overflows and the Disposal of Storm Sewage*, Final Report, Min. Housing and Local Government, H.M.S.O., London, 1969.

[5] Scottish Tourist Consultative Council, *Report by the Working Party on the Caravan in the Environment*, Scottish Tourist Board, Edinburgh, 1973.

[6] K. LIGMAN, N. HUTZLER and W. C. BOYLE, Household wastewater characterization, *Am. Soc. Civ. Eng.*, *Envir. Eng.*, **100**(1), 1974, 201–213.

[7] *Pumping Stations for Water and Sewage*, R. E. Bartlett, Applied Science, London, 1974.

Suggested Further Reading

[1] *Public Health Engineering Practice*, Vol. 1, *Water Supply and Building Sanitation*, Vol. 2, *Sewerage and Sewage Disposal*, L. B. Escritt, MacDonald and Evans, London, 4th Ed., 1972.

[2] *River Pollution 3: Control*, L. Klein, Butterworths, London, 1966.

[3] *Water and Wastewater Engineering*, Vol. 2. *Water Purification and Wastewater Treatment and Disposal*, G. M. Fair, J. L. Geyer and D. A. Okun, John Wiley & Sons, N.Y., 1968.

[4] *Drainage Details in S.I. Metric*, E. L. Wooley, Northwood, 1971.

[5] Manufacturers' catalogues and descriptive literature.

5 Chemical sanitation and physico-chemical treatment

The conventional method of sewage treatment relies upon settlement and the growth of micro-organisms in the sewage to convert small and soluble materials into a larger settleable form. Two alternatives to this procedure are available.

a) addition of chemicals to sterilise and mask the sewage — a conservancy system with the minimum volume of additional water added — Chemical Sanitation.

b) addition of chemicals to cause flocculation and coagulation of the sewage — Physico-chemical Treatment.

The former method is essentially a temporary expedient and the resulting solutions still require treatment before discharge would normally be permitted. The latter method is capable of producing a good quality effluent and can be considered as an alternative to biological treatment.

5.1 Chemical sanitation

Chemical sanitation relies upon the addition of a chemical to kill any micro-organism and effectively sterilize the sewage. The normal use for these chemicals is in treating human wastes and preventing the growth of anaerobic bacteria with the associated odour and health hazards. The wastes are converted into a sterile, more aesthetically acceptable liquid, and should have little or no deleterious effect upon any subsequent sewage treatment process. A minimum volume of water is added to the sewage to reduce the volume of sterilized waste which will require treatment and transport.

Three types of chemical closet are available:

a) Portable — usually a 'bucket' system in which the closet is merely a holding vessel which contains the sterilizing chemical. Once the vessel is full, or after a fixed period, the contents are discharged. The design of these units is covered by B.S. 2081 *Portable closets for use with chemicals* [1]. The units are normally designed to take approximately 25 l (5 gallons); this produces a full vessel which weighs approximately 25 kg (50 lb). Such a weight has to be carried to a disposal point, and 25 kg is considered to be the maximum weight which can be so carried.

It is important in the planning and layout of any site which expects to have some use of portable chemical closets, that the disposal points be conveniently sited to avoid carrying the 25 kg weight over long or difficult distances. The disposal points should be designed to minimize the inconvenience of the emptying process.

This type of chemical closet is widely used in caravans and also finds use on boats, in tents, holiday cottages and isolated dwellings.

b) Recirculating – the solid materials are filtered out and the remaining liquid sterilized with a chemical. The liquid portion, which is sterile and deodorized, is subsequently used as a flushing solution for the closet bowl.

Certain portable recirculating models are available and are used in boats, caravans and tents. The larger versions of this type of closet are also used on aircraft, long distance buses, certain trains and ships.

c) Continuous – the wastes are sterilized directly by chemicals, as in the portable type of closet. The units are particularly designed for recreation areas, car parks, lay-bys and areas which serve relatively large communities but are distant from main drainage, e.g. isolated industrial sites. As the units are expected to be used by the general public, they need to be of robust construction and usually require frequent supervision to ensure continued effective operation. Supervision is usually necessary as much to prevent vandalism and mal-use of the units as to ensure efficient chemical sanitation.

Full details of the design and operation of all these units are available from the manufacturers and suppliers. Of more direct relevance is the type and quantity of the sewage produced by these units and disposal of the wastes.

5.2   Strength and volume of sewage from chemical sanitation systems

The total volume of human wastes produced per day, including solids, is approximately 2 l ($\frac{1}{2}$ gallon). This volume is therefore the minimum volume of sewage generated per person per day by the full use of chemical sanitation facilities. Clearly, if other facilities are used or are anticipated, the volume of chemical sanitation sewage will decrease proportionately: e.g., for a caravan with an average occupancy of 3½ persons, the volume of chemical sanitation sewage would be approximately 50 l/week (12 gallons/week). An equivalent caravan using a toilet block on a main drainage system would generate at least twelve times this volume of sewage from use of the facilities in the toilet block.

The volume of water used per caravan would be similar (45 l/caravan day) for sites with and without a toilet block, provided that an adequate water supply is available. The total volumes of wastewater produced are therefore reduced\but by a smaller factor (3 or 4).

The raw concentrated human wastes which are accumulated in a chemical sanitation unit have a high oxygen demand, B.O.D.$_5$ 8–10 000 mg/l, C.O.D. 20–25 000 mg/l. Thus the discharge of these wastes directly into a biological sewage works can create a very severe demand for oxygen within the aerobic biological unit. Such a shock load is often particularly severe if the pattern of residence at a camping or caravan site creates an optimum disposal time for a significant number of chemical sanitation units: e.g., on a site which normally has a high proportion of weekly residents, emptying on a Friday or Saturday prior to leaving the site can cause a significant shock load.

Thus, although the total B.O.D. per person from sites served or partially served by chemical sanitation is likely to be similar to solely main drainage sites, the volume of sewage is less and the sewage strength is greater. The pattern of diurnal flow can also be distorted. From most stable communities there are simultaneous peak flows and maximum B.O.D. loadings. The erratic disposal of relatively small volumes of highly polluting chemical sanitation liquids can distort the B.O.D. and flow loadings.

5.3 Sanitary fluids

The requirements of sanitary fluids to be used in portable units are given in B.S. 2893, *Chemical preparations for chemical closets*[2] and can be summarized as requiring the fluid to

a) deodorize excreta and continue to do so for one week.

b) obscure the closet contents.

c) be easy to remove from the closet and make the closet easy to clean.

d) be free from objectionable colour, non-injurious, stable and non-inflammable.

While these standards provide adequate safeguards to health and hygiene, there is no mention of the subsequent disposal of the fluid. Certain organizations (e.g. the Caravan Club) have introduced ancillary restrictions which ensure that only fluids which are likely to create few disposal problems are permitted. Certain preparations are marketed which do not meet these latter standards (e.g. caustic soda (NaOH) based products) but which have a restricted and valuable use.

5.3.1 Formaldehyde

The commonest sanitary fluids (Elsan Blue, Racasan) are 10% weight for weight solutions of formaldehyde. These solutions comply with the British Standard and are generally accepted. The fluids also contain a detergent to facilitate cleaning, a perfume to mask odours, a dyestuff to visually mask the closet contents, and buffering agents to ensure that the diluted solutions maintain the pH required for effective bactericidal action. Such a formulation also acts as a deterrent to flies, is non-corrosive and does not have an unpleasant odour.

These fluids are diluted to form the charging solution for a toilet. For the normal use of a 25 l (5 gallon) portable unit, this necessitates diluting the original fluid 1 : 16 then using 2 l ($\frac{1}{2}$ gallon) of diluted fluid in the 25 l bucket. Such a solution usually lasts a family of four for approximately 4 days, and so represents approximately 0.008 l/cap. d of the original sanitary fluid.

Formaldehyde itself exerts a B.O.D.$_5$ of approximately 2 mg/l for each mg/l of formaldehyde. The B.O.D. of sewage treated by these chemicals will therefore be increased by the effects of the residual formaldehyde. The original 10%

formaldehyde fluids have a B.O.D.$_5$ of approximately 200 000 mg/l. After subsequent dilution into 25 l, the solution would have a B.O.D.$_5$ of 1000 mg/l and a total B.O.D.$_5$ of 0.025 kg (cf. 0.054 kg/cap. d total B.O.D.$_5$). In normal use the final concentration of the liquids to be disposed of is reduced significantly (10–20 mg/l). Discharge of these fluids does therefore increase the B.O.D. of sewage. The proportion of this increase depends greatly upon the mode of use of the fluid. If the chemical closets are only emptied when full and when the formaldehyde concentrations have been reduced by reaction with the closet contents, the B.O.D.$_5$ of the sewage should be only slightly increased (<10%).

Sanitary fluids which contain higher proportions of formaldehyde (35% weight/weight) are more likely to give liquids which contain higher concentrations of formaldehyde when discharged.

Formaldehyde based fluids have found wide application in the portable bucket type of closet and in the portable and fixed recirculating units.

Tests carried out on formaldehyde preparations indicate that for dilutions of the original fluid below 1 in 30 000 there is some lag period before micro-organisms can degrade the formaldehyde[3]. At dilutions greater than 1 in 30 000 of the original fluid, degradation proceeds normally. As the original fluid is diluted 200 times to fill a toilet, a further dilution of 150 times is required to ensure adequate microbial action. Under normal conditions of use 10 times dilution with other wastewaters will prevent adverse effects.

These fluids, if properly used and if adequately diluted by normal domestic sewage, should not affect the performance of small biological sewage works. Trials of these fluids on percolating filters and activated sludge treatment plants have confirmed these general conclusions. Problems are more likely to arise from negligent use of the fluids, e.g. emptying the remaining half bottle of neat fluid into a water closet at the end of a holiday, or the shock overloading of a treatment plant. The discharge of a considerable proportion of chemically treated sewage into a sewage works will overload the plant in two ways. A very large B.O.D. load will be imposed upon the aeration capacity of the plant and the concentration of formaldehyde may be sufficiently high that microbial activity is impaired.

It is probably more common to bury or remove by contract the wastes from chemical closets than to add them directly to a small sewage works. However, the tightening of effluent standards, the building of better equipped camping\and caravan sites and the difficulties of contract tanker services at times of peak holiday traffic are expected to put more emphasis on the on-site treatment of this type of chemical sanitation wastes.

5.3.2   Caustic soda

Treatment of toilet wastes with a concentrated solution of caustic soda (sodium hydroxide) sterilizes the liquids and breaks down some of the particles and large molecules. These sanitary fluids are not described in the British Standard[2] and are not fully accepted. The fluids tend to impart some caustic odour to the atmosphere.

Caustic soda based products can be used in portable units. However, it is essential that the units are specially designed non-spilling closets as recommended for these types of fluid. Continuous appliances as used at lay-bys, rest and recreation areas, also employ caustic soda based sanitary fluids.

Products based upon caustic soda rely for their sterilizing action upon a high pH; such conditions cause more serious disposal problems as microbial action is usually severely limited above pH 8.5. It is normally necessary to ensure at least a 50 times dilution factor with normal domestic sewage to ensure adequate biological treatment. The presence of this well diluted caustic soda then only marginally increases the pH of the sewage and microbial action is not impaired. Caustic soda exerts no significant B.O.D. load. Once neutralized to near neutral pH-values it acts solely as added electrolyte, e.g. sodium chloride, sodium sulphate, sodium nitrate and will pass directly through a biological treatment works. The action of the strong alkali in breaking down the structure, particularly of some of the complex molecules in human wastes, does reduce the suspended solids and the B.O.D. of the wastes and makes them more amenable to biological treatment.

The caustic soda treated wastes, after dilution, can also be disposed of via a soakaway pit. Such disposal is usually the only alternative to contracting a tanker service for the large volumes of high alkalinity liquids from continuous chemical sanitation systems.

5.3.3 Phenol/coal tar fluids

Coal tar preparations with and without oil seals can be employed as chemical sterilizing agents. These products contain phenols and act as very effective bactericides.

The prepared solutions have a distinct 'creosote' odour that implies a strong sterilizing action. This odour can be advantageous in general use as an assurance of competent sewage disposal. However, such fluids are usually less acceptable in a confined space, e.g. a caravan.

Coal tar preparations are inhibitory, even at low concentrations, to the microorganisms present in biological treatment processes. Any oil seal material is additionally liable to inhibit the oxygen transfer necessary for aerobic treatment. Discharge of coal tar preparations to biological sewage works is therefore not recommended. Instead, the final solutions require burying, composting with lime and vegetable matter or removal by contract. Although coal tar preparations are described in the relevant British Standard[2], they are not usually acceptable at camping and caravan sites and even at individual sites can present disposal problems.

5.3.4 Miscellaneous chemical agents

A variety of other chemical formulations have been marketed for chemical sanitation. However, none has been as successful as the formaldehyde, coal tar and caustic soda products. The British Standard[2] only describes formaldehyde and coal tar products and at camping and caravan sites formaldehyde products are generally preferred.

Chlorine donors used in relatively high concentrations are sterilizing agents. These products do, however, produce a marked chlorine odour which restricts their use in confined spaces.

Solutions of zinc salts are often employed to produce 4–5000 mg/l of zinc in the charged closet. This high concentration of metal ions necessitates a significant dilution (at least 1/100) with normal domestic sewage to prevent the inhibition of biological sewage treatment. Toxic metals cannot be degraded and tend to accumulate in the waste sludges which require disposal. The presence of significant concentrations of zinc in a sludge seriously restricts certain modes of disposal, e.g. spraying onto agricultural land, which can lead to high concentrations of zinc in crops.

5.4 Ancillary actions of sanitary fluids

Sanitary fluids are employed as expedient measures and are required to maintain public health and hygiene standards in the absence of main drainage. The chemicals are also required to maintain aesthetic standards, notably those of odour, and to provide a final product which can be disposed of easily.

The requirements of sterilizing sewage and easy disposal are partially contradictory. An effective sterilizing agent can only permit the biological growth required for degradation of sewage after sufficient dilution to limit its toxic effects. The availability of adequate disposal facilities for the particular fluids is therefore crucial if large volumes of chemically treated sewage are produced.

Most sanitary formulations contain some perfume additive to mask the odour of the sewage and/or the sanitary chemical. While these odour-masking agents can improve the aesthetic appeal of chemical closets, they can present potential dangers. Effective chemical sanitation relies upon sterilizing the sewage and so preventing the growth of potentially harmful micro-organisms. The sense which detects such growths is that of smell as the noxious gases are given off during the anaerobic decomposition of sewage. Over-zealous masking of odours can therefore hide the indications of potentially dangerous microbial activity. Equally, particularly heavy perfume agents can become unacceptable in enclosed areas.

In addition to sterilizing sewage, the chemicals (particularly formaldehyde) are often deterrents to insects. Particularly in the case of flies, this is clearly advantageous in maintaining public health and hygiene. In caravans, where the separation of toilet and kitchen facilities is likely to be small, any reduction of possible insect-carried infection is advantageous.

5.5 Disposal facilities for chemical sanitation liquids at camping and caravan sites

Operators of camping and caravan sites usually provide separate disposal facilities for the contents of chemical toilets, provided that the site is large enough to warrant the additional construction. The design and layout of such disposal facilities is usually at the discretion of the site operators, and any licensing or controlling authority. It should however be remembered that the full units can weigh in excess of 25 kg. Not all site users are capable or prepared either to carry the units large distances or be able to empty them with ease. The facilities therefore are required to be conveniently situated and require non-slip surfaces for the user, and a properly graded disposal point to minimize contamination.

The operator is then faced with alternative methods of treating the disposed chemically treated sewage.

1) Biological treatment with other sewage at an on site sewage works.

2) Separate disposal of the liquids.

If the chemically treated sewage is to receive biological treatment, it is critical to ensure that only easily biodegradable chemicals are discharged to the works. This usually means that only formaldehyde preparations can be permitted to enter the sewage works. Such a restriction is usually enforceable in controlled communities, e.g. residential or long-stay sites, or sites run by particular organizations. It is harder to control discharges at sites with a more rapid turn over of clientele, or open, or partially open, to the general public, e.g. sites which have a fixed unit − marina, hotel, caravan site, but where the drainage includes a component from a generally accessible unsupervised area − lay-by, rest area, car park, picnic site. In the latter case, the provision of warning notices and supervision is the only recourse to prevent non-acceptable fluids.

Provided that only the easily biodegradable or non-harmful chemicals are included, it is also necessary to ensure that adequate dilution is available at all times. Predictions can usually be made based upon the expected occupancy of a site, e.g. if a site is only 20% caravan stands and 80% tent pitches, the caravans are likely to produce the majority of the chemically treated sewage, and the chance of a serious overload of B.O.D. or chemical is lower than on a caravan only site.

For sites which do not anticipate a possible overloading situation, direct discharge into the sewage works is feasible. For less favourable cases some holding or balancing tank with steady controlled dosing into the sewage or sewage works can be advantageous. Storage of these wastes in a holding tank should not present problems as they contain some residual sanitary chemical. Clearly, if it is feasible to mix these wastes in a controlled manner with the normal domestic sewage prior to addition to the sewage works, such a design is preferable. The details of this additional construction depend upon local topography and site characteristics, but should ensure that the wastes from chemical sanitation have no deleterious effects upon biological sewage treatment.

If separate disposal is to be arranged, the critical parameters are often sizing the holding tank for the chemically treated sewage and arranging adequate ultimate disposal. For relatively primitive sites which do not provide a full range of facilities, chemical sanitation may be the only toilet facility available. It is then merely necessary to arrange for the holding tanks to be emptied by contract or, for removal from the tank and burying usually in trenches, or, composting of the wastes. The choice between these possibilities often depends upon local conditions, availability and frequency of tanker services, land availability, manpower requirements.

Disposal of this chemically treated sewage by any method will influence the volume and strength of sewage to be treated at the sewage works. The modifications of sewage characteristics should be included in the design criteria of the treatment works.

5.6   Physico-chemical treatment

Chemicals can be added which produce a readily settleable floc. This floc contains the majority of the suspended and colloidal matter present in sewage. Settlement of the chemically treated sewage produces a clear effluent which can be further purified to reduce the $B.O.D._5$ of the soluble fraction. The major chemicals employed are lime $(Ca(OH)_2)$, alum $(Al_2(SO_4)_3)$ and ferric chloride $(FeCl_3)$. While the effectiveness of these chemicals is similar, costs vary between different countries; in Britain lime is usually cheapest. The addition of small quantities of synthetic polyelectrolyte usually helps to produce a compact, more readily settleable floc which provides an effluent very low in suspended solids. Comparison between treating a weak sewage by conventional activated sludge processes and pilot plant physico chemical treatment after primary settlement, is shown in Table 5.1.

Table 5.1   *Treatment of raw sewage by conventional activated sludge plant and pilot scale physico-chemical methods.*

		Averaged Analysis mg/l.	
	Raw Sewage	*Activated Sludge Final Effluent*	*Physico-chemical Treatment Effluent*
Suspended Solids	100	10	10
$B.O.D._5$	200	15	60
$B.O.D._{30}$	400	75	210
Phosphate	5.5	5.0	0.1

Effluents from this basic form of physico-chemical treatment are usually comparable in quality with the conventional biological treatment, but do not fulfil the often quoted 30 : 20 Royal Commission standard. The $B.O.D._5$ of the effluents is often greater than that normally expected. In order to reduce the $B.O.D._5$ of the effluent so as to fulfil the 30 : 20 standard, some form of tertiary treatment is required. This is likely to be an activated carbon column to adsorb soluble organic materials but could be grass plot irrigation.

Small scale physico-chemical treatment has only recently become available and is as yet unproven in general use. For small and variable communities it has several advantages.

a) The process can be automated and requires little maintenance.
b) Variations in hydraulic and B.O.D. load have little effect upon the treatment efficiency. Similarly, the process can start up quickly.
c) Biologically toxic materials have no effect.
d) Phosphates are removed simultaneously.

The process is, however, largely untried in on site situations, and sufficient expertise is not yet available on the operation and maintenance of the plants. The amount of solids produced in the sludges will be higher than for biological processes, as no organic material is degraded. Without some form of tertiary treatment, the $B.O.D._5$ of the final effluents is likely to be greater than 30 mg/l.

References

[1] B.S. 2081: 1954, *Portable Closets for use with Chemicals*, British Standards Institution, London, 1954.
[2] B.S. 2893: 1957, *Chemical Preparations for Chemical Closets* (Portable Type), British Standards Institution, London, 1957.
[3] *Elsan Blue Double Strength Sanitary Fluid Technical Bulletins*, Elsan Ltd., London, 1966.

6 Cesspools and septic tanks

6.1 Cesspools

The water borne sewage transport schemes used in large communities have largely been provided to overcome the problems associated with individual sewage collection, storage and treatment. The use of a pit which collects sewage is centuries old. The principle is that the increased surface area allows percolation of sewage through the subsoil — the original version of 'out of sight, out of mind'. Apart from the obvious unsanitary problems of fly infestation, stench and fouling of surfaces caused by overflowing pits, there is the more insidious transference of disease by organisms spreading through the subsoil. This may contaminate underground water sources and there also exists the possibility of rendering such sources unusable due to the transference of nitrogen compounds from sewage forming nitrate ion in the water.

The word 'cesspool' is a legal term used in the Public Health Act 1936, the British Standard CP 302 : 200 (1949) general series and in Building Regulation N 17. Confusion exists because the legal definition of a cesspool in the 1936 Public Health Act, covers septic tanks and settlement tanks. In this book, however, the following description is felt to be more appropriate, i.e. a cesspool is an underground chamber constructed for the reception and storage of foul water (i.e. water contaminated by faeces or urine). Some of the requirements of a cesspool are, that it shall be impervious and not overflowing, that it shall have a minimum capacity of 18 m^3 and can be completely emptied, and that it shall be adequately covered and ventilated.

Further details of construction are adequately covered by the above publications. The cesspool is therefore simply a storage facility which requires periodic emptying and is not intended to be used as a tank wherein decomposition of settled material occurs (i.e. it is not a septic tank).

The capacity of the cesspool suggested by CP 302 : 200 is not less than 45 days whereas Building Regulation N 17 gives 18.2 m^3. However, it is common for tankers of approximately 3.2 m^3 capacity to be used to empty the cesspool. Assuming 2 persons each using 180 l per day, the cesspool would require to be emptied completely every 50 days. The cost of such a service based on figures supplied by various Scottish Local Authorities in 1974 would be approximately £4 per trip or £160 per year unless this is included in the general rate. In addition, the initial cost of excavation and the concrete construction must be considered. At 1975 prices the excavation could be between £3/m^3 and £5/m^3 with the construction being £950 (1975). An alternative fibreglass cesspool of

18.2 m^3 capacity from Klargester Environmental Engineering would be between £550 and £800. Hardstanding and tanker access has to be provided to a distance of perhaps 20 m from the tank. It can be seen from the foregoing figures that in many cases the small unit of perhaps one or two households may consider that a somewhat greater capital outlay on a septic tank − percolating filter − tertiary treatment scheme may be worthwhile.

6.2 Sludge digestion tanks

A septic tank is a chamber in which solids settle out and, under suitable circumstances, undergo digestion. The effluent is then more suitable for treatment by a percolating filter which will not tolerate large quantities of suspended solids without blockage (see Chapter 8). The processes occurring in septic tanks are poorly understood and partly due to their unaesthetic qualities their study is likely to remain sparse. The following is not an exhaustive discussion but is intended, by considering large scale processes first, to point out major features of the process.

The digestion or liquefaction of high organic content settled sewage is utilized in many sewage works. The principle can be considered as the facultative breakdown of proteins, carbohydrates, fats and oils into acids, alcohols, aldehydes etc. In a heated digester a build up of anaerobic methane-fermenting organisms will occur which will then produce a mixture of methane and carbon dioxide of calorific value 22×10^3 kJ/m^3. This gas is largely produced in a continuous mesophilic (32°C) digester within 20 to 25 days. The rate of gas production is very slow at lower temperatures, and under cryophilic or cold digestion the gas is not usually collected. In a large scale sewage works using cold digestion, the retention time (capacity/input) can be very long with the digestion process probably ceasing during the coldest of the winter months. The digestion process, therefore, is carried out on the organic material by bacteria which are sensitive to a wide range of materials, such as detergents, disinfectants and heavy metals, surface active agents often have the most deleterious effect.

Although the design and operation of heated digesters require considerable expertise and control, unheated cryophilic digestion has been used for more than 70 years, both for small and large scale treatment of sewage sludges.

6.3 Imhoff tanks

The tank bearing the name of this eminent German public health engineer has been used for many decades. The design of such tanks has been modified and imitated to such an extent that only the basis of the system will be discussed further. Although the use of Imhoff tanks has been superseded for large works by heated digesters, their use in original or modified forms for small works continues throughout the world.

The tanks were often used as primary settlement tanks incorporating cryophilic digestion. The gas mixture produced had to be collected to be vented to air, simultaneously being prevented from stirring the contents of the

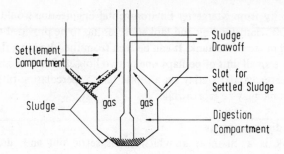

6.1   Diagrammatic representation of an Imhoff tank.

settlement tank. The simplified diagram (Fig. 6.1) indicates how the settlement tank was separated from the digestion tank by an inverted funnel. The solids entered the settlement tank and during a retention period of up to 4 h duration they dropped onto the cone and hence slid down to the slot and finally to the digestion area at the base of the tank. The overflow rates for the settlement tank are of conventional primary settlement tank magnitude (see Chapter 7) as also are the weir overflow rates. The solids which reach the bottom of the tank digest producing gas which rises to the underside of the cone and then to the scum 'chimney'. Since the gas will entrain some solids on rising, an overlap between the downward projection of the lip of the cone and the sides of the digestion compartment is built into the tank to prevent scum formation in the settlement tank. The sludge is removed at long intervals using a hydraulic head of approximately 1–2 m. The gas produced can be stored and burned or allowed to escape to air. The escape of gas is sometimes accompanied by foaming which necessitates a considerable (0.5 m) freeboard of the vent aperture above the settlement tank water level. The effluent from the settlement tank can be expected to produce removals of suspended solids of 50 to 70% and B.O.D. reductions of 30–50%. Much greater percentage reductions are sometimes quoted. However, unless details of the method of sampling are given, it is difficult to confirm the significance of such results.

The use of Imhoff tanks for larger installations has greatly reduced in favour of the heated digester. The problems associated with the Imhoff tank can be stated as follows:

   a) the use of cold digestion in Imhoff tanks does not produce sufficient methane/carbon dioxide gas quickly enough to compete with mesophilic digesters;
   b) the depth necessary to accommodate the digestion tank under the settlement tank can produce problems in difficult soils;
   c) occasionally offensive odours can be released;
   d) transference of solids to the settlement tank from the digester can occur by excessive gas production causing foaming or boiling.

However, tanks based on the principle of a settlement tank over a cold digestion tank can provide compact treatment units which are simple in operation and hence require little maintenance. In addition, they would have the advantage of long periods of sludge accumulation and storage between desludging.

6.4 Septic tanks

The problems of deep excavation and the complexity of construction of Imhoff tanks can be avoided by allowing both settlement and digestion to occur in the same tank; such a tank is a septic tank. It consists essentially of a tank or, in more modern versions, a series of tanks in which settlement of solids occurs. The liquor has a considerable retention time, compared to a settlement tank in a large works, with the intention of maximizing solid deposition. Three regions are present in the tank. Firstly, a scum which forms a crust on the surface of the tank; secondly, the liquor from which solids are being deposited and into which solubilized material is diffusing from the third layer, consisting of solids settled out and digesting. Inlets and outlets are usually simple dip pipes or baffled weirs which are intended both to prevent scour of settled material and to avoid disturbance of the surface scum. The effluent from a septic tank is greatly in excess of the usual 30 : 20 :: S.S.: B.O.D standard, thus some further treatment is required. On a small scale this is often a percolating filter unit with tertiary treatment.

6.4.1 Sizing of tanks

The design criteria suggested in CP 302 are intended to cover installations to treat up to 300 persons; however, in parts of the world where discharge is to a sea loch or coast, the use of septic tanks for much greater numbers is not unusual. With increasing stringency of effluent standards, such installations may be reduced in number in the future. The present discussion is concerned mainly with tanks for populations up to 300. The present design in CP 302 is $C = (180 P + 2000)$ litres where C is the tank capacity in litres and P the population number.

Assuming a flow of 180 l/cap. day, this gives retention times of greater than 3 days for a minimum of four people, to 25 h for 200 people. The previous suggestions (CP 302 : 100) gave the capacity equation as

$$C = (30 P + 400) \text{ gals}$$

$$\text{or } C = (136 P + 1800) \text{ litres.}$$

The increase from 1956 is to take account of greater water usage. The most important point is that the sizes are based on a true dry weather flow, i.e. the exclusion of water other than domestic usage. The building regulations 1965 give a minimum capacity of 600 gallons, which agrees exactly with the CP 302 : 1972 sizing procedure for the minimum of 4 people. The amount allowed to prevent surges from scouring bottom material is increased slightly from 1800 l (400 gal) to 2000 l (440 gal). Other workers have suggested somewhat different size criteria; however, in the absence of accurate information about flow rates, it is suggested that the code be followed after allowing for garbage grinders (70 l per head served) or other local effects.

The simplest form of tank can be either rectangular section or can be designed on a circular shape using prefabricated concrete pipes. This latter system is interesting because it would produce three compartments in series which should effectively reduce carry over of sludge. One drawback to this system is that the hydraulic characteristics of a cross diameter flow circular tank could be very inferior to a conventional rectangular tank. However, since the retention time in septic tanks is extremely long, the material could settle quite efficiently in such a system designed for a small population on the basis of CP 302. The authors have been unable to find such a tank in operation; however, the results for such a tank are given by Nicoll[1] from a previous work, and therefore the reader is referred to the original paper for further information.

The simplest form of tank suggested by CP 302 consists of a rectangular tank in series with a square section tank, the first tank having a length/breadth ratio of 2 : 1, both tanks having minimum depths of 1.5 m. In order to simplify construction, the use of a baffle placed $\frac{2}{3}$ of the length along a tank with a ratio of length/breadth of 3 : 1 is also described. Considerable argument exists over the relative efficiencies of multiple chamber tanks. A recent American survey suggests little significant statistical difference in effluent standards between single and multiple chambered tanks. Evidence from other workers is difficult to interpret since too many factors are varying simultaneously. The overall settlement of material is unlikely to be improved; however, in septic tanks sludge which has settled can rise due to trapped gas bubbles. In this case a separate in-series compartment is advantageous. The bulk of the deposited material will be settled out in the first compartment and the rising sludge problem will occur more often in the first compartment. The use of the second compartment, therefore, guards against this occasional problem.

6.4.2   Overflow rates and weir overflow rates

Much of the discussion in Chapter 7 dealing with settlement tanks is pertinent to septic tanks; however, the size is so small as to render meaningless discussions of overflow rates per day. The weir overflow rates, however, are likely to cause problems of surging with the use of dip pipes on the outlet. Assuming a 100 mm diam. outlet dip pipe and a population of 30, the maximum surge could probably be estimated as 3 W.C.'s flushing in unison, each using approximately 9 litres and all flushing within 10 seconds. This flow rate gives a weir overflow rate equivalent to approximately 742 m^3/m day. A conventional primary large scale tank overflow rate would be 220 m^3/m day at maximum flow. Assuming a peak flow to be possible in a small septic tank for the same population but using a weir length of 1.3 m (assuming a depth of 1.5 m) the overflow rate at the weir is approximately 180 m^3/m d. This rate is presumably often encountered in large scale tanks designed to a specification of 220 m³/m d for 3 D.W.F. and is more satisfactory.

The surface overflow rate is given by

$$O.R. = \frac{180\,P \times \text{Depth(m)}}{180\,P + 2000} \text{ in } m^3/m^2 d$$

At a depth of 1.5 m the overflow rates for populations of 10, 30 and 100 are 0.7, 1.1 and 1.4 m³/m² d assuming the flow to be equally spread throughout the day. Allowing for the admittedly unlikely situation of $\frac{1}{3}$ of the population using W.C.'s simultaneously, the overflow rates would be equivalent to approximately 62, 95 and 117 m³/m² d for the respective populations. The maximum is less than 4 times the common design figure for primary tanks at 3 D.W.F. The figures above are equivalent to a (peak flow)/(flow averaged over the day) ratio of 87 : 1. Such a situation is probably unlikely and peak/average flow ratios of $\frac{1}{3}$ this value are probably more realistic. On this basis overflow rates at peak flows are unlikely to be unsatisfactory.

6.4.3   Scum and sludge production

The production of a surface scum is not only accompanied by an improvement in effluent quality but may, by trapping surface material, effectively help the operation of the tank. Experiments under controlled conditions on purely domestic waste indicate that scum build up from unseeded (i.e. clean) tanks requires a number of months before an effective accumulation of sludge and scum is present. The design basis given in CP 302 assumes a sludge capacity of less than 12 months. In other conditions the time between desludging periods can be 3 or 4 years or under unusual circumstances the tank may be desludged only after very long intervals. The data to hand indicates that some deterioration in effluent quality may occur if desludging is neglected. A suitable period would be between 9 and 12 months. More important, however, is the necessity to leave a proportion ($\frac{1}{6}$) of the sludge to seed the process in the first compartment. The second compartment should be emptied completely as its role is to avoid carry over of rising sludge from the first compartment. Under these circumstances the sludge and scum will occupy less than 50% of the tank volume.

Assuming a suspended solids inlet value of 450 mg/l and a removal of 70% by settlement, this is equivalent to 0.057 kg/cap. day at a flow of 180 l/cap. d. Assuming 30% digests over a period of 9 months, this is equivalent to approximately 0.04 kg/cap. The moisture contents of sludges and scum vary depending on length of time since desludging, the efficiency of digestion, the presence of detergents etc.; however, an overall figure of 10 to 12% solids content would give a volume of sludge of 0.4 l/cap. d to 0.33 l/cap. d. Over 9 months the sludge volume accumulation would be approximately 110 l/cap. (24.2 gal). This is in rough agreement with other authors' comments; however, it should be stressed that the presence of excessive amounts of detergent and the

Table 6.1 (from [2])   *Effluent quality from septic tanks*

Period	Effluent parameter	Control tank	Experimental tank
1	B.O.D. mg/l	218	217
	S.S. mg/l	101	97
2	B.O.D. mg/l	173	180
	S.S. mg/l	106	106
3	B.O.D. mg/l	152	206
	S.S. mg/l	87	87

Period 1 (June 1964–January 1965) No detergent added. Scum and sludge initially absent.

Period 2 (January 1965–May 1965) 20 mg/l detergent added to influent of experimental tank only.

Period 3 (May 1965–July 1966) 50 mg/l detergent added to influent of experimental tank only.

over-zealous use of cleaning agents can change these quantities by either reducing the effect of digestion or by causing a greater precipitation of suspended material.

6.4.4   Effluent quality

Table 6.1 lists the results of an investigation into the operation of septic tanks by Truesdale[2]. The problems associated with obtaining a meaningful statistical analysis of determinations of $B.O.D._5$ and S.S. on a system suffering wide diurnal variations in flow with large surges of suspended solids inlet concentrations and relying in part on a solids digestion system which is sensitive to daily temperature fluctuations, are enormous. The authors are therefore content to suggest that average reductions of $B.O.D._5$ and S.S. within the ranges 30–50% and 50–70% should be looked for. If the results after the first year's operation are not of this standard, a check should be made of the operational circumstances and water usage.

A survey of septic tanks carried out on Ministry of Works installations is reported by Nicoll[1]. These indicate average effluent $B.O.D._5$ concentrations in two compartment septic tank installations between 93 and 166 mg/l, whereas for single compartment tanks, values of 160 to 278 mg/l are quoted. In both cases the best results are quoted for tanks which have been desludged within 6–12 months of being tested. It is of interest that the mean retention period quoted in the above publication seems to have little correlation with B.O.D. or S.S. effluent quality. This is possibly because the time allowed for settlement is more than adequate even in the case of the shortest retention times.

As a general rule, the following points should be noted:

a) the use of strong bactericidal cleansers should be discouraged by householders discharging to a septic tank. If they are used, they should not be discharged without some form of dilution;

b) the use of unnecessary amounts of detergents should also be discouraged, as it can reduce the solids removal efficiency of the tank;

c) the crust should not be removed when desludging the tank. In the older tanks with the inverts sloped towards the inlet the removal of sufficient sludge could be achieved with minimum disturbance to the crust. However, since the greater proportion of settled material will be deposited in the first third of the tank, even flat bottomed tanks can be desludged without greatly destroying the crust. If the crust is completely removed, it may require more than a year for it to be re-formed.

References

[1] E. H. NICOLL, Aspects of small water pollution control works, *J. Inst. Publ. Hlth. Engrs.*, Issue 12, Nov. 1974, 185–211.

[2] G. A. TRUESDALE and H. T. MANN, Synthetic detergents and septic tanks, *Survr. Munic. Cty. Engr.*, 9th Mar. 1968. 28–30 and 33. Water Pollution Res. Laby. Reprint, 539.

7 Settlement processes

7.1 Introduction

The concentrations of suspended solids found in domestic sewages range from less than 200 to more than 450 mg/l. The removal of a large proportion of these solids by settlement alone is relatively easily and cheaply accomplished. Primary settlement of sewage prior to aerobic oxidation often removes 60–70% of the suspended material which accounts for 30–40% of the sewage B.O.D. The following classes of material are settled or screened in a sewage works.

a) Grit: a hard inorganic material which enters the sewage through road and floor washings. Being of greater specific gravity than most organic material, it settles easily and can form grit banks, scour penstocks and thus cause nuisance in the works. The amount is variable; however, its removal is often not required in small scale works operating on a totally separate system.

b) Organic material including faecal waste, some of which will be colloidal in nature or so small as to be impossible to settle in the conventional flow system of a sewage works.

c) Silts and clays too small to be classed as grit but easily settled in conventional works.

d) Secondary sludges, i.e. those produced in the aerobic treatment processes. The sludge from a percolating filter is referred to as humus sludge and the following settlement tank as a humus tank.

e) Rags, papers, etc. which are usually removed by some form of screen and are then referred to as screenings. It is convenient to class the material under headings a) to d) according to their settlement behaviour.

7.1.1 Class I settlement

The particles attain a constant settlement velocity in the first few seconds and thereafter settle at this 'terminal velocity'. A plot of particle height above the channel invert versus time would under ideal conditions be a straight line. For a discrete (i.e. totally separate non-interacting) spherical particle settling under laminar flow conditions the settlement velocity is given by:

$$v = \frac{gd^2(SG - 1)}{18v}$$

where v = settlement velocity (m/s)

d = diameter of particle (m)

g = acceleration due to gravity (m/s^2)

58

SG = specific gravity of the particle (dimensionless)

ν = kinematic viscosity of particle (m^2/s).

For most conditions, therefore, the settlement velocity will be proportional to the diameter squared and the specific gravity minus one. In larger works the grit is allowed to settle in channels or tanks whilst the mean forward velocity is kept >0.3 m/s in order to scour organic material and thus prevent its deposition. Apart from proprietary devices, the simplest form of settlement is attained in a grit channel with length to depth ratio of approximately 18 : 1 with trapezoidal section which approximates to a parabola. This latter shape has the advantage that the forward velocity can be stabilized at 0.3 m/s ± 20%, irrespective of flow depth. On smaller works of less than 2000 population equivalent it is often unnecessary to make separate provision for grit removal and to remove the grit when servicing the plant. This is assuming a totally separate system with little, if any, run off from paved areas, roofs etc.

7.1.2 Class II settlement

This includes material which interacts or flocculates and thus changes its diameter with time. For such material the plot of height of particle above the invert versus time is a curve as shown in Fig. 7.1. Sewage, however, is extremely variable in nature and does not lend itself to a theoretical approach to the design of settling facilities as in the case of grit settlement.

7.1.3 Zone settlement

Activated sludges settle in an unusual manner which fortunately aids the removal of fine material. If a litre sample of sludge is shaken and allowed to settle an almost clear liquid phase will separate out above a sludge-solids interface. At the bottom of the cylinder a zone of compression of the sludge will form, and above this a zone of lower sludge concentration can be identified. Under these circumstances it is meaningless to consider the settlement of separate particles and therefore the liquid/sludge interface height is usually plotted versus time as in Fig. 7.2. The depth to which this interface settles in 30 mins is the basis of the sludge volume index (Section 2.4). The extent to which the liquid phase is clear

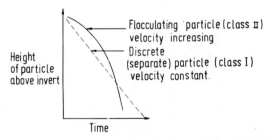

7.1   Discrete (class I) and flocculating (class II) particle settlement.

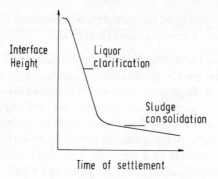

7.2   Settlement of activated sludge.

of smaller particles determines how clear the effluent will be and to a large extent what the effluent B.O.D. will be. The concentration to which the sludge will settle in a given time determines the volume to be returned to the aeration tank. The settlement and clarification behaviour of the sludge is a function of the many process parameters used in the aerobic oxidation stage.

7.2   Design criteria

The design criteria for grit have already been dealt with; however, for sewages it is more useful to have an idea of how much material will settle in a given time rather than how a definitive particle will settle. This can be estimated by means of a batch settlement analysis. In this test a homogeneous suspension of sewage is placed in a long tube. Samples are taken at different depths and times and the percentage of particles remaining in the sample is plotted versus the upward flow velocity (depth/time of sampling). A typical plot is shown in Fig. 7.3. For any value of the velocity V_0 there will be a percentage of particles x_0 which will have settling velocities greater than V_0. In an upward flow tank this will represent the theoretical removal of particles at any chosen design velocity V_0. For a horizontal flow tank there will be a further fraction of particles which will be removed. This extra proportion can also be determined from Fig. 7.3[1].

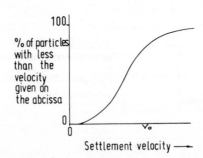

7.3   Cumulative settlement curve for discrete particles.

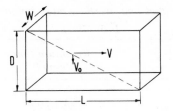

7.4   An idealized settlement tank.

7.2.1   Overflow Rates

From a consideration of Fig. 7.4, the design settlement velocity V_0 in an ideal tank can be taken as that velocity which is the property of that type of particle which is completely removed in the tank.

By geometry
$$Q = VDW;$$
$$\frac{V}{V_0} = \frac{L}{D}$$

where
V = mean horizontal velocity
D = depth and W = width of tank
L = length of tank
Q = flow through tank.

$$\frac{Q}{V_0DW} = \frac{L}{D}$$

$$V_0 = \frac{Q}{\text{Surface Area}}, \ldots \tag{7.1}$$

i.e. these particles, 100% of which will be removed in the tank, have a settlement velocity V_0 to equal the flow per unit area of the tank.

This simple formula (7.1) has lead to the adoption of overflow rates per unit area, or mean upward flow velocity, to describe tanks. Conventional values were based on 600 gals/cu ft/day or 4 ft per hour. These values in S.I. units are 30 m³/m²d and 0.339 m/s; however, this latter precise conversion suggests an accuracy of design which was not observed in practice. The overflow rate or upward flow velocity can be converted into retention time by considering the depth or capacity of the tank. Such values as those given above refer to overflow rates and velocities at full flow which is normally taken as 3 dry weather flow + 1.1 trade waste for large works. Table 7.1 gives values for both retention time and overflow rates commonly in use. The figures for septic tanks and settlement tanks are calculated on the basis of design given in CP 302.

Table 7.1   *Retention times and overflow rates commonly used (at maximum flow rates).*

	Retention time (hours)	Overflow rates $(m^3/m^2 d)$
Primary settlement*		
prior to percolating filter	$1\frac{1}{2}$ to 2	30–45
prior to activated sludge	1 to $1\frac{1}{2}$	
Humus tank settlement*	$1\frac{1}{3}$ to $1\frac{2}{3}$.	35–40
Activated sludge settlement*	$1\frac{1}{2}$ to $1\frac{3}{4}$	45–60
Extended aeration sludge		
settlement CP 302	–	22
Septic tanks CP 302	>24	–
Settlement tanks CP 302		
(primary)	>15	–
Humus tanks CP 302	>4	–

*In the past, much greater retention times have been common for large scale practice.

7.2.2   Weir loadings

In addition to the use of overflow rates and retention times, a further design parameter is used which defines the maximum overflow rate of effluent per unit length of weir. This limit is necessary as too great an outlet weir loading rate (or an inlet weir loading rate) can considerably alter the hydraulic characteristics of the tank. Clements[1] and other authors have drawn attention to this factor and in the former case have attempted to correlate the loss of ideality of the tank flow due to poor inlet and outlet design. Table 7.2 gives values of the weir loading rates commonly applied in large scale works. Suggested values are also given for extended aeration sludge settlement and small scale humus tank settlement.

7.2.3   Tank shape

The choice of a particular shape of tank is often based on factors such as local soil conditions, convenience of sludge removal or cost of construction, none of

Table 7.2   *Weir loading rates for large scale practice (at maximum flow) and suggested small scale rates.*

	Weir loading rate $(m^3/m\ d)$
Primary settlement	<220
Humus settlement	<200
Activated sludge	<250
Small scale:	
Humus settlement	<100
Extended aeration	<100

which are related to the efficiency of the settlement processes occurring in the tank. In particular, small scale or package plants often use designs which, while they may be convenient from the construction viewpoint, are at the same time incapable of operating efficiently in the context of a small works suffering rapid large hydraulic flow fluctuations. The following is of necessity a generalization which is particularly pertinent in small works.

Two types of settlement tank are: upward flow and horizontal flow. Upward flow tanks are particularly useful for many industrial processes. However, they are somewhat less efficient than horizontal flow tanks when dealing with a heterogeneous input. The upward flow tank is commonly met with in small works as part of a package plant where they act as secondary settlement tanks. Experiments on such a tank[2] shown in Fig. 4.2 indicate that when hydraulic surges occur in the tank, the velocity at the bottom of the tank (see Fig. 4.2) is sufficiently great to cause failure of the settlement process. Because of the problems of design and operation, upward flow tanks are not recommended for construction without specialist advice. Horizontal flow tanks are very commonly used in small works, where they are usually rectangular. In larger installations, removal of the settled sludge becomes increasingly important and circular tanks are often preferred. In large rectangular tanks the sludge is pushed to one end of the tank by a travelling or continuous scraper mechanism which can also be used to remove surface scum. In a circular tank usually involving outward flow to a peripheral weir, the sludge is continuously scraped to the central well by blades suspended from a radial gantry driven by a motorized wheel at the periphery. There is also a scum blade offset and attached to the gantry to remove surface grease etc. With small settlement tanks of the type described in CP 302 there is insufficient sludge to warrant a scraper mechanism. In this case it is usual to adopt a sloped floor to aid in collection of the sludge.

One advantage of a circular tank using outward radial flow lies in the increased weir length and hence lower weir overflow rate compared with a horizontal tank with the same surface area. However, due largely to the problems of constructing circular tanks, they are not often used for small works.

7.3   Primary settlement

The most common primary tank found in small sewage treatment works, which is not part of a package plant, will probably be a horizontal flow tank, being rectangular in plan with a sloped invert. The following discussion is intended to explain the principles behind the choice of operational and design parameters, in order to give the reader a better insight into settlement tank processes and to aid in making rational choices in those circumstances where CP 302 is inadequate. The settlement tanks suggested in the above publication will be used to explain different criteria. While the initial settlement processes occurring in septic tanks or modified Imhoff tanks are explained by the same principles as for settlement tanks, they are intended to digest or liquify some of the solids so settled and necessitate separate discussion (see Chapter 6).

7.3.1   Applicability

Settlement tanks cannot be used to store sludge for periods much greater than a week and, depending on the type of sludge, desludging at less than weekly intervals may be necessary. The process of cold digestion which is used in septic tanks can occur in a settlement tank leading to gas formation which in turn causes the sludge to rise. This will automatically increase the solids carried over the outlet weir. A regular and complete desludging of the tanks is essential at weekly intervals. In many circumstances the availability of labour to empty and desludge the tanks cannot be relied upon, in which case septic tank or package plant installations are suggested. It is unlikely that such labour would be available in a community of less than 100 and, in these circumstances, a septic tank plus percolating filter is preferable.

7.3.2   Sludge volumes and moisture content

In a survey[3] of many large sewage works the amount of primary sludge production alone averaged 0.055 kg/cap. d. Although it is notoriously difficult to determine accurately the removal of suspended solids by settlement, it is probable that 60–70% are removed in many tanks. Assuming an inlet concentration of 325 mg/l S.S., this would give for a water usage of 180 l/cap. d approximately 0.058 kg/cap. d S.S. Assuming 65% removal, this would give 0.038 kg/cap. d dry sludge solids which is considerably below the survey figure. The moisture content of the sludge from the tank will vary depending largely on operational techniques; however, working on 96% M.C. for a sludge drawn off at weekly intervals, the volume would be approximately 6.6 l/cap. week or 0.66 m^3 per week per 100 population. The regular treatment or disposal of this volume of sludge must be considered prior to the choice of a settlement tank.

7.3.3   Capacity and shape

The capacity of the settlement tank described in CP 302 is 100 l/cap. or 15 h retention time based on a flow of 161 l/cap. d. Using 180 l/cap. d, a capacity of 100 l/cap. would give a retention time of 13.4 h. Although batch settlement tests of primary sewage indicate that little if any extra settlement would occur within the extra 1.6 h, the design should be at least based on 15 h retention to allow for poor hydraulic characteristics in the tank. In certain circumstances it may be possible to foresee or to estimate from past measurements that the flow would be much greater than 180 l/cap. d, in which case the retention time forms a better design basis. The time of 15 h also happens to be the same as the recommendation made by the 5th report of the Royal Commission on Sewage Disposal[4] for continuous flow tanks operating on a dry weather flow basis.

   The tanks originally considered in the theory earlier in this chapter were ideal and did not suffer scouring, and hence resuspension of settled material. In practice, primary sludge will scour at velocities greater than 32 mm/s. In order to avoid scour and allow for sludge storage, CP 302: 1972 suggests a minimum depth of 1.2 m. from T.W.L. to the invert at the exit end of the tank.

Clements[1], however, has shown that the choice of a low length/depth ratio can lead to increased scour assuming that the length/breadth ratio has been set. For a population of 200 with 100 l/cap. capacity split between two equal sized tanks, the dimensions would be approximately 1.2 m deep; 1.7 m wide and 5.1 m long for each tank, neglecting the wedge shaped section below the exit invert. The considerations given by Clements are unsatisfied by this procedure. It is advisable, therefore, not to increase the depth much beyond 1.2 m. The length/breadth ratio of 3 : 1 suggested by CP 302: 1972 has been chosen with the intention of increasing the ideality of the flow through the tank. Generally, for a given type of inlet, the flow pattern is improved by making the tank long and narrow; however, by so doing, the overflow rate at the weir is increased. For the same tanks for 200 population with a length/breadth ratio of 2 : 1, the weir overflow rate would be 7.95 m^3/m day compared with 11.0 m^3/m day for a tank of the same depth (1.2 m) and same flow (160 l/cap. d) but with length/breadth ratio of 4 : 1. These figures assume that the flow is regular, whereas in small scale tanks the variations can be much greater than in large tanks. The choice of length/breadth ratio of 3 : 1 will leave considerable leeway to allow for fluctuations of flow.

7.3.4 Inlets

Work by several authors has shown that failures in inlet design can adversely affect the flow through the tank and hence reduce its efficiency. Experiments on full scale tanks[5] have shown that the flow is not necessarily in the same direction at different depths. In small scale tank design the problem is of greater importance due to hydraulic fluctuations. CP 302: 1972 suggests the use of a simple four outlet flow splitter. Although this is better than a single inlet for each tank, it has the drawback that the inlets are angled on entry to the tanks. An arrangement which the authors consider better is described by Nicoll[6] and consists of a drowned slot. This has the advantage of using the whole width of the tank, thus lowering the inlet velocity. The aims of an inlet system can be summarised as follows:

    a) to reduce the velocity of the fluid entering the tank,

    b) to diffuse the incoming fluid over as wide an inlet area as possible,

    c) to prevent the setting up of deleterious hydraulic flow such as short circuiting or side flows.

7.4 Secondary settlement tanks

Much of the previous discussion also applies to humus tanks and activated sludge settlement tanks. Humus tanks for small schemes are described in CP 302: 1972 in a similar design system to primary tanks. The design basis of

$$C = (30\,P + 1500)\ \text{litres}$$

where P = population

      C = capacity in litres

gives retention times of 2.3 days for $P = 4$ to 4.7 h at $P = 300$ assuming a water useage of 180 l/cap. d. These figures are well in excess of the design figures used in large works and are intended to allow for surges. The necessity for desludging the humus tanks still exists, however, and therefore use of such a tank for small populations is unsatisfactory from the maintenance aspect even though its use could produce a more satisfactory effluent. The tank should be desludged at weekly intervals or less and therefore the use of a settlement tank – percolating filter – humus tank scheme lends itself to a regular maintenance and desludging schedule.

The quantity of sludge produced in a humus tank is subject to considerable variation especially in the early spring, however the survey referred to earlier[3] found, approximately 0.027 kg/cap. d. The sludge produced is more watery than primary sludge and like the primary sludge its M.C. will depend on the ability and expertise of the labour available. Assuming an average moisture content of 97% the sludge production could be in the range 0.8 l/cap. d to 1 l/cap. d, or approximately 600 l/week per 100 population.

The sludge produced from rotating disc processes is settled out in tanks which operate in similar manner to septic tanks and it is inappropriate to discuss this here (see Chapter 9).

An interesting fact concerning the effluent from humus tanks, treating percolating filter effluent, or high rate plastic media effluent is the straight line produced by a plot of solids remaining in suspension after settlement versus B.O.D. in the effluent. Provided the tanks are designed with adequate capacity the most likely causes of excessive effluent suspended solids and hence high effluent B.O.D. values are irregular, incomplete or tardy desludging.

Activated sludge settlement has special requirements not shared by either primary or humus sludge settlement. Not only has the supernatant liquor to be clarified in order to produce low effluent S.S. and B.O.D. values, but the sludge has to be thickened as much as possible to avoid returning larger quantities of liquid effluent than is necessary. Activated sludges, and more particularly sludges from extended aeration processes settle badly, often giving final moisture contents of greater than 99% (this figure is equivalent to 10 000 mg/l dry solids). The return of 1 kg dry S.S. to the mixed liquor in a slurry of 99.5% M.C. requires the pumping of 0.2 m^3 of effluent and reduces the effective volume of the aeration compartment.

7.5 Package plants
In small works the majority of activated sludge settlement tanks are presented as part of a package plant. The choice of shape is limitless and often appears to have been chosen to fit the convenience of the designer rather than the theoretical principles regulating sludge settlement. Since activated sludge is a complex system of living organisms which can change their degree of flocculation with variations in the treatment process operating parameters, some changes in settlement criteria are necessary for extended aeration plants. In

addition problems associated with the scaling down of settlement tanks are aggravated by the increasing ratio of peak flow/dry weather flow found in most small plants. The following discussion is intended to indicate some of the problems associated with small package plant settlement procedures.

The role of the settlement tank and its efficiency in producing a clarified effluent largely determines the effluent characteristics. The failure of many small settlement tanks to operate efficiently has lead to the requirement for tertiary treatment facilities to be included after the settlement stage. Most of the tertiary treatment methods are principally methods which remove suspended solids from the effluent and, by so doing, also remove a proportion of the B.O.D. The settlement zone is usually integral with the package plant and often consists of a baffle, slot or pipe leading to the settlement tank or stilling box. The thickened sludge may be returned to the aeration compartment by gravity feed or, preferably, since a compressor is already available for the aeration stage, an air lift pump can be used. In large scale works the settled sludge is usually mechanically scraped to a central well and transferred back to the aeration compartment by pumping. In contact stabilization plants using a circular settlement zone, the use of scrapers is justified e.g. Satec R diffused air plants. However the expense and power requirements are not justified for small plants and this usually means that the slopes of small package plant settlement tanks have to be steeper than approximately 50° in order to allow the sludge to slide down the sides. The return of the settled sludge back to the aeration stage must be achieved efficiently to prevent the formation of nitrogen bubbles in septic sludges leading to flotation of the sludge. Whilst the concentration of the settled sludge is low this is easily achieved, however, problems can occur if the mixed liquor concentration is too high. Under such conditions the sludge builds up in the settlement tank and solids are discharged over the outlet weir with the next hydraulic surge. Downing *et al.* [7] have shown the correlation between high mixed liquor suspended solids and high effluent suspended solids. In order to prevent this effect it is common for sludge to be abstracted from the settlement zone periodically and stored in a separate aerobic digestor (see Chapter 10.)

The choice of slope of the tank sides can produce problems with overflow rates. The overflow rate required by CP 302 is less than $22 \text{ m}^3/\text{m}^2\text{d}$ or approximately 0.25 mm/s velocity. This compares with the widely accepted figure of $30 \text{ m}^3/\text{m}^2\text{d}$ (0.34 mm/s) for large scale tanks, all figures relating to maximum rates of flow. A pyramidal tank, sketched in Fig. 7.5, designed to fulfill this overflow rate requirement at the surface would give overflow rates of 39; 88 and $350 \text{ m}^3/\text{m}^2\text{d}$ at $\frac{1}{4}$, $\frac{1}{2}$ and $\frac{3}{4}$ tank depth at peak flow rate in a true upward flow tank. For this reason it is common to allow the top third of the tank to be vertical sided.

CP 302, while suggesting overflow rates, makes no mention of weir loading rates. The assumption that any weir loading rate is satisfactory is fallacious since weirs that have their length effectively reduced by rags, uneven settlement etc. give rise to poor effluents. On large scale tanks weir loadings of $150 \text{ m}^3/\text{m}^2\text{d}$ can

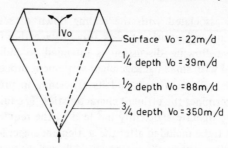

7.5   Variation of velocity with depth in an upward flow tank.

be quite efficient however with an extended aeration sludge and the inevitable hydraulic inadequacies of small scale tanks, overflow rates of less than 100 m³/m d should be used. One design that achieves a large weir length to overflow area is the Inka Bioreactor described in Chapter 5, where use is made of an inboard weir to effectively double the weir length. The reduction in weir length by rags and other materials can be avoided by a good maintenance schedule, the problems associated with uneven settlement can however be more serious and lasting. In order to combat this adjustable jacks may be provided or as in the case of the Satec A-D type plants, an adjustable weir is incorporated into the plant.

References

[1] M. S. CLEMENTS, Design of rectangular sedimentation tanks on velocity principles, *Survr. munic. Cty. Engr.*, 19th Oct. 1968, 41–45.

[2] D. BARNES and S. A. ASHIE, Personal communication 1974.

[3] *Public Health Engineering Practice*, Vol. II, *Sewerage and Sewage Disposal*, L. B. Escritt, McDonald & Evans, London 1972, 494 p. Based on the Report of the Water Pollution Research Laboratory; Survey of the Performance of Sewage Sludge Digesters throughout England, Scotland and Wales. D. G. SWANICK *et al.*

[4] *Royal Commission of Sewage Disposal*, 1901–15, Ten Reports and Appendices, H.M.S.O. London.

[5] S. G. BURGESS and A. F. GREEN, More detailed examination of flow in sewage tanks using radio-active tracers, *J. Inst. Sew. Purif.* 1960, Pt. 2, p. 184–194.

[6] E. H. NICOLL, Aspects of small water pollution control works, *J. Inst. Publ. Hlth. Engrs.*, Issue 12, Nov. 1974, 185–211.

[7] A. L. DOWNING, G. A. TRUESDALE and A. E. BIRKBECK, Some observations on the performance of extended aeration plants. *Survr. Munic. Cty. Engr.*, Sept. 12, 1964, 29–34A.

8 Aerobic treatment processes

8.1 Introduction

Sewage treatment is intended to produce well stabilized or well oxidized material in the effluent. A well oxidized effluent should contain little food source for aerobic bacteria. The discharge of the effluent to a river should therefore lead to little removal of dissolved oxygen by bacterial action. In order to achieve a well oxidized effluent, one of two aerobic treatment processes is usually used: percolating filters or activated sludge.

Percolating or trickling filters carry out the purification process by contacting aerobic sewage with a stationary film of organisms growing on a supporting medium. The type of medium employed, the geometry of the system and choice of batch or continuous process treatment offer a wide scope for different designs, as will be discussed later.

The activated sludge system involves the contact of free floating organisms (the activated sludge) with the sewage. In order to keep the system aerobic, the mixture is oxygenated.

It is possible to use a combination of the above two processes as in the less common submerged bed system where a submerged filter is in contact with aerated sewage.

Neither of these systems lends itself to easy biological characterization of the organisms involved. The activated sludges vary with the way the plant is operated and with the substrate (i.e. the composition of the sewage). The percolating filter also shows considerable variation in biological types present in the film. In this latter case there is a further complication, namely the presence of larvae and worms which play an important role in keeping open the voids in a conventional filter.

Although the activated sludge plants can, under ideal operating conditions, produce Royal Commission 30 : 20 effluent standards, the problems of settling the fine flocs produced in this process make some form of tertiary treatment advisable. Percolating filter effluents require some form of settlement in order to separate out the humus which sloughs off the filter, or for smaller schemes the humic material can be removed by trickling over grassland, pebble bed clarifiers or other methods.

8.2   The activated sludge process

This is a continuous aerobic oxidation process utilizing free floating organisms. The process can be described best by the aid of a diagram such as Fig. 8.1. The sewage entering the activated sludge aeration zone has to be mixed with sludge returned from the final settlement tank. The suspension is then aerated to keep the oxidation process going and simultaneously the suspension is agitated to prevent deposition of solids in the tank. After a retention time of a few hours to perhaps two days, the mixture reaches the final settlement tank where the sludge settles and is returned to mix with the incoming sewage, whilst the clarified liquid is taken off by a weir (see Chapter 7). In carrying out the oxidation, the micro-organisms multiply and some method is usually employed either to store the excess sludge produced, or to treat and dispose of it. In many of the plants discussed in Chapter 15, the two processes of aeration and settlement may take place within the same tank, a settlement zone often being within the aeration tank with baffles being used to produce a quiescent volume. The purification process is complex and poorly understood; however, a simplified description would include the following:

a) an adsorption mechanism which occurs in the first half an hour and which probably continues slowly over the next few hours as adsorption sites become available again;

b) a continuous reaction performed by the bacteria leading to the oxidation of the organic matter into: carbon dioxide (CO_2), water, (H_2O) phosphate, (PO_4^{111}) sulphate, (SO_4^{11}) nitrate (NO_3^{1}) etc.

c) the use by the bacteria of polluting material to produce new cellular material, i.e. the activated sludge itself.

These three reactions should be almost complete by the settlement stage. Here the sludge must be separated from the effluent since the sludge itself consists of organic material which can be oxidized and hence could exert an oxygen demand on a receiving water. Having settled out the sludge, the process can begin again when this settled sludge is mixed with fresh incoming sewage. It is fortunate that this process can be operated continuously, the amount of sludge being regulated on large and small works by bleeding off the excess. It is most important that the following points be understood fully.

The process can be initiated either by allowing the sludge to grow 'naturally'

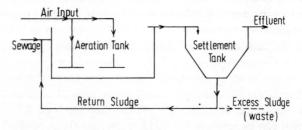

8.1   Diagrammatic representation of the activated sludge system.

in the sewage works, or by obtaining *activated* sludge from the nearest sewage works. The word 'activated' is stressed since unfortunate cases have occurred where a 'digested' sludge has been used by mistake. This is totally unsatisfactory. The activated sludge itself varies according to the sewage characteristics; however, for an operating plant, control of the sludge condition is achieved by manipulating process parameters such as aeration loading, B.O.D. loading, settlement and aeration times etc. One cannot approach manufacturers and buy in selected organisms; the whole process must be considered as a dynamic biological balance between many factors which, in badly designed plants, may include regular hydraulic washout of organisms leading to a reduction in process efficiency.

The production of new cellular material cannot be prevented; however, under very low substrate loadings the sludge production can be minimised (see Chapter 10). This is the basis of the 'extended aeration' system. The sludge returned from the settlement tank is regulated in most works; that which is in excess can be stored aerobically and periodically disposed of. Despite the previous comment that the sludge itself can exert an oxygen demand, the B.O.D. input, output, loading and removal figures ignore this factor. The B.O.D. relationships throughout a plant are based on the implication that the sludge itself does not exert a B.O.D. while carrying out the purification process. The retention times quoted in British literature almost always refer to a nominal retention time in the aeration tank obtained from the ratio of tank capacity to the sewage inflow. The flexibility of this process together with its compactness has led to its rapid adoption not only for large scale treatment but also for small package plants.

8.2.1 Variations in the basic process

If the sewage is mixed with the sludge and aerated for a short period of time ($\frac{1}{2}-1\frac{1}{2}$ h), the adsorption process mentioned earlier takes place, giving rise to a partially purified effluent after final settlement. The sludge must now be aerated for a number of hours prior to mixing with fresh sewage. This aeration allows the sludge time to metabolize the adsorbed material. Such a process is called 'contact stabilization'. The advantages lie in the reduced tank volume requirements of the process. This process is not generally used for communities less than 2000 population.

In the 'conventional' activated sludge process as used in many large works, the retention time in the aeration tank is greater than that of the contact stabilization process, being 8–12 h. This is a nominal figure. There may be a short period of reaeration of the returned activated sludge.

Extended aeration is a process whereby, as its name implies, the aeration period is increased to at least 24 h. The underlying principle is that in the later stages of the aeration process, the sludge, having used up its food source, will then begin to break down itself, undergoing endogenous respiration or auto oxidation. The advantage claimed is that the sludge production is less than in a conventional system. Table 8.1 gives a comparison of the various systems in

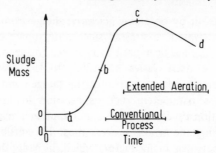

8.2   Activated sludge growth curve.

terms of their operational parameters. The loadings and other information in Table 8.1 p. 76 are indicative of the operating ranges of the processes.

8.2.2   Kinetics of the processes

It is common to explain the kinetics of the activated sludge process by means of the type of diagram shown in Fig. 8.2. Although many reservations must be held against this simplified picture of the process, its utility lies in the fact that it gives a picture of what is an extremely complicated biological process. If a pure bacterial culture is grown, the number of organisms often follows the relationship with time shown as o to d in Fig. 8.2. The various stages could be labelled as:

o–a   lag phase while organisms adjust to a different substrate type; this may not be present;

a–b   logarithmic growth rate, substrate in excess;

b–c   reduction in *rate* of growth, food becomes limiting;

c–d   breakdown of the organisms – autoxidation.

Eckenfelder[1] has given reactions for different parts of this type of curve for the growth of sludges in sewage treatment and has suggested that conventional and extended aeration treatment operate over the ranges as shown in the diagram, i.e. extended aeration involves a greater period of time in the auto oxidation stage. Contact stabilization does not fit into this system since the kinetics are more determined by adsorption rates than oxidation rates.

The curve shows a decreasing rate of growth from b to c and it is within this range that most package plants operate. For these conditions Eckenfelder has suggested that two equations are applicable, the first being used for B.O.D.$_5 > 300$

i.e.
$$L_r = \frac{K_1 S_a t}{a}$$

L_r = the B.O.D. removed

K_1 = const.

S_a = the average sludge concentration over the period considered.

a = fraction of B.O.D. transferred to new cells (often between 0.5 to 0.65)
t = time of reaction.

When the B.O.D.$_5$ of the liquor drops below 300, the process will become exponential of the type

$$\frac{L}{L_0} = e^{-k_2 S_a t}$$

k_2 = a const.
L = the B.O.D. at any time.
L_0 = the initial B.O.D.

Strictly all the B.O.D. values referred to above are ultimate B.O.D. values where

$$L_{ultimate} = \frac{\text{B.O.D.}_5}{1 - 10^{-k_1 5}}$$

k_1 is a constant which is approximately 0.15/day for sewage at the temperature of a B.O.D.$_5$ test (20°C). Therefore the B.O.D.$_5$ is approximately 86% of the B.O.D.$_{ultimate}$.

Although these equations indicate that the removal of B.O.D. would follow a relationship indicated by that shown in Fig. 8.3 they do not lead to conclusions which can easily be adopted for design purposes. The most important parameters have been suggested in a Ministry memorandum[2] and also in CP 302: 1972. Since the parameters are somewhat dependent on aeration processes, they will be discussed later.

8.2.3 Aeration processes

In large scale works a number of aeration systems can be used, e.g. surface brushes or paddles, turbine aerators, diffuser domes etc. For small scale plants the requirements are low maintenance, low operational noise levels and economy. Two factors predominate in the transportation of O_2 from air to the sewage. One is the capacity of the aeration system, i.e. the rate in kg/h at which

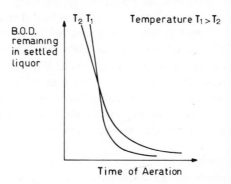

8.3 B.O.D. removal versus time of aeration for the activated sludge system.

the operator can transfer O_2 into the liquid; this depends largely on the rate at which new air-liquid interfacial area can be produced. The second is the economy of the process, i.e. the mass of oxygen transferred to the liquid per unit of energy expended. Downing[3] and others have drawn attention to these two factors. Fortunately, the loss in economy for an improvement in capacity is not extreme. In most small scale works the most critical factor is the need to keep the process operating with the minimum of supervision. Since clogging of diffuser domes is common in large works, small scale plants often use simple wide orifice pipes, holes drilled in lateral tubes or vibrating leaf spring aerators. The economy for these systems is often less than 60% of the value of 1.7 kg O_2/kW h commonly accepted for large scale aerator efficiency. The oxygen requirements can be calculated on the assumption that the plant is operating under extended aeration conditions where 2.0 kg O_2 are required for each kg B.O.D.$_5$ removed. The daily per capita B.O.D.$_5$ production can be estimated as 60 g. Working on 2.0 kg O_2/kg B.O.D.$_5$ and an economy of 0.8 kg O_2/kWh this gives a power requirement of approximately 0.15 kWh/cap. d. An assumption has been made that all the B.O.D.$_5$ has been destroyed, which is not correct but the calculation gives power requirements of the correct order of magnitude. Manufacturers and franchise holders often quote efficiencies or economies which have been obtained under conditions so different that direct comparison is meaningless. However, reputable firms will often translate their figures into kWh/cap. year and compressor ratings which can be compared for the same type of process. It is important to note that for a conventional sewage treatment scheme where little oxygen is required for sludge autoxidation and nitrification, the oxygen requirements can be reduced to between 0.9–1.2 kg O_2/kg B.O.D.$_5$ removed whilst for a roughing process where the sewage is only partially treated, the oxygen requirement is further reduced. It is therefore necessary for the buyer to ensure that the power requirements quoted by the manufacturer are for the particular process being considered.

The concentration of dissolved oxygen in the tank is also important. If too little is applied in the early stages of treatment, the process will be inefficient and under extreme conditions the sludge may go anaerobic; if too much oxygen is present in solutions, poor settlement of the activated sludge may occur. An overall figure of 1–2 mg/l dissolved oxygen is usually satisfactory. The use of tapered aeration may be incorporated into the tank system. This method of aeration allows more air to be transferred to the liquid in the initial stages of treatment with a subsequent lessening of air input in the later stages. This can be achieved by a simple process of diminishing the number of diffusers or orifices down the length of the tank. In very small scale treatment systems the compact and fully mixed nature of the treatment makes tapered aeration inapplicable.

8.2.4 Oxidation ditches

Although these operate on an activated sludge treatment system, they have certain specific qualities which make it advisable to consider them separately. In essence they are oval ditches about 1–1.25 m deep, wherein activated sludge is contacted with sewage. Instead of aerating by diffusers or pipes, it is more common to use a surface rotor or brush which is nowadays usually made of stainless steel. The wave action caused by the brush aerates the liquor and a velocity is imparted to the mixed liquor to keep the solids in suspension.

The types of procedure used to settle the sludge can vary from a separate sludge settlement tank to a removable baffle placed across a compartmented half width of the aeration channel. CP 302 gives a capacity of 260 l/cap. d which is equivalent to 1.45 days retention time based on 180 l/cap. d. However, retention times greater than this value are usual. The value for the oxygenation capacity of the rotor of 110 gO_2/cap. d is obtained from the assumption of 55 g B.O.D.$_5$/cap. d input and a requirement of 2.0 kgO_2/kg B.O.D.$_5$ destroyed to achieve a well stabilised effluent. If the B.O.D.$_5$ is likely to be increased beyond 55 g/cap. d due to garbage grinders etc., the oxygenation capacity must be increased.

8.2.5 Operational parameters for activated sludge plants

Table 8.1 gives the operational parameters for extended aeration activated sludge plants based on the recommendations of CP 302: 1972.

Extended aeration plants are to have an aeration retention time of 1.3 days minimum assuming 180 l/cap. d. However, Downing *et al.* [3] showed that longer retention times, of the order of 3 days, improved the effluent quality. However, the most critical parameter was the build up of high mixed liquor suspended solids concentrations leading to sludge loss. Present design, therefore, is often based on a retention time of less than 2 days with detailed attention paid to the wasting of excess sludge. In order to keep the M.L.S.S. between 2000 and 5000 mg/l as Downing suggests, sludge should be wasted at regular intervals as follows:

assume a per capita B.O.D.$_5$ production of 0.060 kg B.O.D.$_5$, with a flow of 180 l and a per capita aeration tank volume of 360 l. The total B.O.D.$_5$ removal could be $0.060/180 \times 10^6 - 20$ mg/l.

This would be 313 mg/l or 313/333 × 100%, i.e. 94% B.O.D.$_5$ removal.

Using a rough figure of 0.5 kg new cellular material produced per kg B.O.D.$_5$ removed; the sludge solids produced per capita would be given by:

$$313 \times 180 \times 0.5 \text{ mg/d.}$$
$$\text{i.e. } 28\,170 \text{ mg/d.}$$

In a per capita volume of 360 l, this would represent a daily increase of M.L.S.S. of 28 170/360 mg/l d or 78 mg/l d.

Because the effluent probably contains up to 30 mg/l S.S., the above value may be reduced to, perhaps, 65 mg/l d. If the M.L.S.S. originally has a concentration of 2000 mg/l, it would take approximately (5000–2000)/65 days for the M.L.S.S. to reach 5000 mg/l. Therefore, after approximately 46 days, the

Table 8.1 Operating parameters for conventional and extended aeration activated sludge processes.

	Retention Time (Nominal)		B.O.D.$_5$/sludge loading kg/kg M.L.S.S.	Air required m^3 air/kg B.O.D.$_5$ removed	O$_2$ required for B.O.D. removal kg/kg B.O.D.$_5$ removed	Main aeration tank. Capacity per head l	Sewage pre-treatment
	Main Aeration tank h	Sludge aeration h					
Conventional	6–12	0–0.5	0.25–0.6	40–70	1.0–1.2	40–90	Usually >1$\frac{1}{2}$ h settlement
Extended aeration	24–72	none	0.05–0.15	187 (2.7 m deep) 280 (1.8 m deep)	1.8–2.2	>230	Usually none

aeration contents would have reached 5000 mg/l M.L.S.S. which is a suitable upper limit. At this stage, sludge should be wasted to reduce the M.L.S.S. down to 2000 mg/l. If the secondary settlement stage produces a sludge of 99.0% M.C., the sludge volume requiring removal would be given by:

$$360 \frac{(5000 - 2000)}{10^6 \times 10} \text{ m}^3 \text{ or } 0.108 \text{ m}^3/\text{cap. at } 99\% \text{ M.C.}$$

If the sludge were taken from the aeration compartment, the volume to be removed would be

$$360 \frac{(5000 - 2000)}{10^6 \times 5} \text{ or } 0.216 \text{ m}^3/\text{cap.}$$

This figure is equivalent to approximately one gal/cap. d excess sludge at a concentration of 5000 mg/l.

However, it is somewhat unsatisfactory to allow the system to be operated on this 'seesaw' principle since, with small package plants, one has very little information regarding actual concentrations of M.L.S.S.

An alternative method of operation would be to remove sludge from the settlement compartment at daily intervals, and to store this sludge in an aerobic digester. This principle is used in the Inka package plants. The quantity of sludge removed can be calculated from data similar to that assumed in the above calculation. This method has the advantage of producing a stable M.L.S.S. concentration.

The aeration requirements are 15.5 m^3 per day (air) per capita for a tank of depth 2 m to 10 m^3 per day (air) per capita for a 3 m deep tank. This seeming paradox is due to the increased transfer efficiency in the deeper tank. This can be explained as follows:

The amount of O_2 required per capita is approximately 0.110 kg O_2/d. However, air contains only 21% O_2 by volume and the transfer efficiency is poor for the coarse bubble aerators found in small scale tanks. Therefore, assuming that 24 m^3 air at 20°C contains 3.2 kg O_2, a transfer efficiency of 5.3% would mean an air requirement of 15.5 m^3 per head. The greater efficiency of transfer in the deeper tank (e.g. 8.3%) transfers the same oxygen but uses less air. The poor efficiency of the aeration systems has previously been commented upon.

The two interrelated parameters, namely B.O.D. loading per unit aeration volume and B.O.D. loading per unit mass mixed liquor solids, can be considered together. If the M.L.S.S. is 4000 mg/l and the sludge loading rate 0.05 to 0.15 kg B.O.D.$_5$ per kg M.L.S.S., the volume required for a per capita B.O.D.$_5$ loading of 0.055 kg B.O.D.$_5$/d is between 275 l and 92 l. At 2000 mg/l M.L.S.S., these figures would be doubled. In most cases the M.L.S.S. would be unknown and the most sensible method is to assume that a minimum of 2000 mg/l M.L.S.S. would be used with a loading rate of 0.10 kg B.O.D./kg M.L.S.S. giving an aeration volume of approximately 260 l. In practice, after severe hydraulic washout, this value of 2000 mg/l M.L.S.S. can be very much reduced.

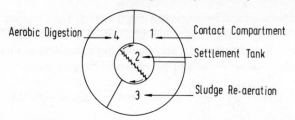

8.4   Diagrammatic representation of a circular contact stabilization plant.

8.2.6   Contact stabilization

In practice the plants are usually circular and divided into four compartments as shown in Fig. 8.4. Compartment number 1 is the contact aeration compartment where the sludge is mixed with the incoming sewage. After settlement in the inner tank 2, the sludge is re-aerated in a separate compartment 3 ready to be passed to compartment 1 after metabolizing the B.O.D.$_5$ adsorbed. A further sludge storage and aerobic digestion compartment 4 is usually provided (see Chapter 10). The combined capacities of compartments 1 and 3 should not be less than 114 l i.e. $18\frac{1}{2}$ h retention assuming a flow rate of 180 l/cap. d. These plants, however, are becoming common for relatively large communities of 2000 population up to 20 000 population equivalents. In such circumstances there will be much greater input of non domestic water; the plants will have to treat the incoming sewage in much the same way as a conventional sewage works. For small scale plants which do not have significant quantities of surface water, the volumes suggested by CP 302: 1972 mean that the plant is not operating in the mode discussed by Eckenfelder[1]. It is the authors' opinion that true contact stabilization installations are inapplicable to the small communities considered in this book and that expert advice should be sought if such a plant is considered.

8.3   Percolating filters

Conventional percolating filters or trickling filters, as their name indicates, consist of beds of stone, usually 2 m deep, which are sprinkled with sewage. Organisms grow on the stones and by adsorption and oxidation reactions purify the waste. The filter size varies from a few cubic metres using a simple corrugated channel to spread the sewage, up to several thousand cubic metres beds with travelling spreaders.

A typical percolating filter would be 2 m deep; the bottom 0.2 m of 250 mm diam. stones, the rest being 60 mm diam. The stones should be of a good quality, hard wearing and weathering stone preferably locally available, e.g. blast furnace slag or broken stone or gravel. The diameter of the stone chosen has increased latterly as it is believed that larger voids are less easily blocked by the film growth which can be of the order of 3–4 mm thick (see B.S. 1438: 1948). The filter is usually equipped with floor tiles to produce adequate drainage with ventilation pipes connected to the underdrains allowing air to circulate through the filter. In operation, a green surface coating of algae appears on the stones;

however, it is the brown slimy covering deeper in the bed which effects the purification. 'Ponding' of filters is due to the heavy growths of micro-organisms blocking the voids and may be avoided by not overloading the filters. As the word implies, ponding means the inability of the filter to allow the sewage to percolate through the stones due to blockage of the voids. In severe cases pools of water can be seen on the bed. The conventional filter described above can be operated in the following way.

8.3.1 Conventional loading
After primary sedimentation (or septic tank treatment), in order to reduce the suspended solids to the filter, the sewage is fed at approximately 0.1 kg B.O.D.$_5$/m^3 d and 0.47 m^3/m^3 d. After treatment, the effluent is passed to a humus tank (see Chapter 7) or in small scale systems to a polishing process.

8.3.2 Recirculation and alternating double filtration
In this process, effluent is returned to the input to the filter and the loadings can be increased to 0.14–0.22 kg B.O.D.$_5$/m^3 d and 0.8 m^3/m^3 d. A further process called Alternating Double Filtration can be used for larger schemes. Should a conventional filter become overloaded, the commissioning of a new filter would take a few weeks. The principle of ADF is that a second filter is already in commission by receiving a low B.O.D. loading. The order of the two filters can be reversed as in Fig. 8.5; the original second filter is immediately capable of oxidizing the applied B.O.D. whilst the original first filter is underloaded with the resultant shedding of excess film growth. The switching process can be repeated indefinitely. Under this system, increased loadings of up to 0.22 kg B.O.D./m^3 d can be used, which is approximately twice that for conventional single pass filtration. Two important disadvantages to this method which usually make it unsuitable for small schemes are the need for pumping facilities and the increase in number of humus tanks required. CP 302: 1972 gives details of percolating filters for small sewage treatment works.

8.3.3 Conventional percolating filter design
CP 302 suggests a conventional percolating filter preceded by an in series septic tank to remove most of the larger suspended solids. The sizes suggested have

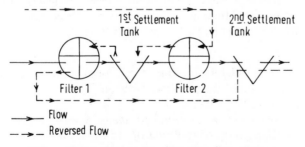

8.5 Alternating double filtration flow diagram.

Table 8.2   *B.O.D. and hydraulic loadings on percolating filters sized according to CP 302: 1972 (Assuming 180 l/cap. d and 0.037 kg B.O.D.$_5$/cap. d).*

Population	B.O.D.$_5$ loading	Hydraulic loading
	(kg/m^3 day)	(m^3/m^3 day)
Up to 10	0.027	0.18
10 to 49	0.034	0.23
50 to 300	0.045	0.30

been discussed by Nichol who has suggested a volume to population ratio of $V = 1.5\ P^{0.8}$ where V is the volume of filter in m^3 and P is the population. This equation smoothes out the irregularities inherent in the sizing procedure given in CP 302 whereby the volume for $P = 9$ was less than the volume for $P = 11$ and similar discrepancies occurred between population numbers of 40 and 60. The B.O.D. loadings implied by these volumes are low compared with those for a conventional filter. Table 8.2 gives values of B.O.D. and hydraulic loading for different values of P; assuming the septic tank effluent to be 150 mg/l B.O.D.$_5$ with an average flow of 180 l cap. d. As the figures in the table indicate, the single pass filter is unlikely to be overloaded and should not require any maintenance other than that mentioned in Chapter 14. The use of roughing filters to relieve overloading works or to achieve partial treatment of sewages is sometimes of importance in small works although it is more usually found in larger works where its ability to handle large flow rates and/or strong B.O.D. influents is its main advantage. These filters come in a range of shapes, some having more regard to the inventiveness of the manufacturer than to theoretical considerations. Common types are Flocor RC, Cloisenyle, Surfpak etc. The materials have very high specific surface areas (surface area per unit volume) and void ratios (ratio of voids to total volume). Their large voids mean that they will accept much coarser material than conventional filters, whilst their high specific surface areas give large film growths per unit volume. They can be stacked in high towers sometimes greater than 7 m due to their low weight per unit volume. The major disadvantage from the point of view of small works is that they do not operate well at the relatively low B.O.D. loadings found in sewage and will not generally produce a Royal Commission standard effluent, although some recent work has indicated that this may be achieved with large scale recirculation of effluent with consequent increase in pumping costs.

References

[1] W. W. ECKENFELDER, Jr. Kinetic relationships in the bioxidation of sewage and industrial wastes, Proc. 14th Ind. *Waste Conf. Purdue Univ., Ext. Sew.*, **104**, 1959, 495.

[2] *Technical Memorandum on Activated Sludge Sewage – Treatment Installations Providing for a Long Period of Aeration*, Min. Housing and Local Govt., H.M.S.O. London, 1969, SBN 11 750215 4.

[3] A. L. DOWNING, G. A. TRUESDALE and A. E. BIRKBECK, Some observations on the performance of extended aeration plants, *Survr. Munic. Cty. Engr., Sept.*, **12**, 1964, 29–34A.

[4] E. H. NICOLL, Aspects of small water pollution control works, *J. Inst. Publ. Hlth. Engrs.*, Issue **12**, Nov. 1974, 185–211.

9 The rotating biological filter

9.1 Introduction

The loss of hydraulic head through a percolating filter (approximately 3 m) often precludes the use of such a process unless pumping can be employed. Pumps are expensive, require yearly maintenance checks and are to be avoided if possible. In the last two decades, the Rotating Biological Filter (R.B.F.) process has been extensively used to overcome this problem. Instead of percolating downwards through stones, the sewage in a R.B.F. moves horizontally through a tank in which large diameter thin discs rotate. Approximately 40% of the surface area of the discs is in contact with the sewage at any time. As the discs rotate, the sewage is adsorbed onto the biological film which grows on the discs and then contacted with air. Oxygen is transferred to the film and bio-oxidation takes place. Because the movement of the sewage is almost horizontal, the head loss through the tank is small. A motor is required to turn the shaft supporting the discs, but this can be small (less than 2 kW) since the shaft is well balanced.

Because this process is becoming increasingly popular, it will be described in further detail in this chapter.

9.2 Description of the Process

Unlike extended aeration schemes, the R.B.F. requires some primary removal of solids. This may be accomplished by separate primary settlement tanks or septic tanks, or a settlement tank which may be incorporated into the unit as in the Ames Crosta Biodisc. In this plant, the settlement tank operates in a way which shows some similarity to the Imhoff tanks described in Chapter 6. Primary settlement may only be used if labour is readily available (see Chapter 7). In common with a percolating filter, material will slough off the discs and therefore the effluent must be clarified by some form of settlement, gravel bed clarifier etc. The R.B.F. itself consists of a shaft carrying a large number of discs sufficiently spaced to allow growth of film without interdisc bridging. Depending on the disc material, this spacing can be 15 to 35 mm. The discs can be from 1 m to 3.5 m diameter and may be made of expanded metal or braced plastics. The shaft is rotated by a low powered motor at approximately 1 r.p.m. for a 2 m diam. disc. The tank bottom is usually contoured to fit the discs closely (2–5 cm gap) in order to encourage plug flow. The discs are grouped into 4 or 5 stages of 20 or more discs, and the flow may be cocurrent or alternately co- and counter current through these stages. The direction of flow appears to be of greater importance in the type of plants where the settlement tanks are situated under the R.B.F. and the liquor can gain contact with the discs through slots in the bottom of the trough. The stages are usually separated by baffles and slots, and there are rarely less than 4 stages.

The R.B.F., like the percolating filter, requires an initial period of several weeks for the organisms to grow. A greater mass of organisms is usually present in the first stage, with different types of organisms predominating on different stages, as bio-oxidation of the sewage proceeds. In addition, the types of organisms change; bacterial cells giving way to protozoa, rotifers and other higher organisms as the purification state achieved in each stage improves. Considerable evidence suggests that the removal of carbonaceous B.O.D. is logarithmic with number of stages, similar to the percolating filter where it was logarithmic with depth. Therefore the use of large numbers of stages cannot be justified except where considerable nitrification is required. Manufacturers delight in producing figures to show that the mass of organisms growing on the discs is equivalent to mixed liquor suspended solids of tens of thousands of mg/l, compared with the activated sludge process which is often between 2000–5000 mg/l M.L.S.S. Such comparisons are meaningless for a small sewage works owner who should consider the overall volume requirements and other design criteria.

9.3 Design criteria
Several factors influence the ability of the R.B.F. to produce good quality effluents. However, much of the information is extremely difficult to interpret due to non uniformity of conditions. Furthermore, in several cases quoted in the literature, plants are underloaded and produce considerable nitrification in addition to good B.O.D. and S.S. removal. In the future, however, it is possible that many companies of doubtful origin may produce R.B.F.'s which may seem financially attractive by being under-designed. The following discussion sets out to review the design of the R.B.F. in order to give a basis for comparison between different plants.

9.3.1 Disc speed
The disc not only serves to aerate the film but also is responsible for aerating the liquor itself and, by causing shear forces, it also causes material to slough off the discs. In most circumstances, the dissolved oxygen level will be sufficiently high if the discs are rotated at a peripheral velocity of approximately 5–7 m/min. If nitrification is required, the speed may be increased in order to ensure that the dissolved oxygen concentration is greater than 2 mg/l. The dissolved oxygen level increases towards the latter stages; however, under the speeds quoted above, a lower limit of 1 mg/l should be achieved in all but the first stage.

One problem which can occur is that of stoppage due to mechanical or electrical failure. Apart from drying out the film with consequent reduction in process efficiency, unless the failure is realized early, the torque required to start the unbalanced shaft can be very large. This argues strongly for a slipping clutch device; some form of failure warning system and, in the case of schools, camp sites, etc., some adequate security to prevent children from jamming the discs with wooden spars or similar material.

9.3.2 Temperature effects

As with percolating filters, nitrification and general efficiency is improved by increasing the operating temperature. In the case of the R.B.F., the relatively thin film of liquid would be prone to freezing, were it not protected. It is therefore common to house the discs. There is also evidence to support the view that the R.B.F. operates more efficiently during the summer; happily, this coincides with the period when most camping sites are suffering their greatest load.

9.3.3 Flow rates

Small works suffer considerably from large variations in flow rate (see Chapter 4), and the ability to cope with such flows is often achieved by overdesigning the capacity of the system. However, the R.B.F. is similar to the percolating filter in that it can cope with considerable variations. The R.B.F. unit has shown itself to be capable of sustaining good performance either with cyclic increases of load such as those occurring in a diurnal flow cycle, or with pulsed flow increases. Flows of up to 400% of the design flow have been applied to an R.B.F. which has only shown serious deterioration of effluent quality after several hours at this flow rate. However, prolonged increases in flow rate, perhaps as a result of underdesigning the original unit, will lead to poor performance. It should be noted also that, in common with extended aeration treatment, the overall effluent standard achieved is determined by the functioning of both bio-oxidation stage and settlement stage. Good quality effluents cannot be achieved from units where the secondary settlement stage is underdesigned. When a pulse increase in flow occurs, liquor at the latter stage of the R.B.F. appears to be displaced. Since this liquor is already well treated, the effluent standard does not diminish greatly. If the pulse duration is small, e.g. a few minutes, the effluent quality will not be significantly affected.

9.3.4 Toxic and other materials

Most plants have to cope with the chance thoughtlessness of the people in the community served by the works. A small Forestry Commission works, for example, suffered intermittent oil discharges. While this indicates the need to instruct the community in what may or may not be discharged, it also implies that any small works must be capable of dealing adequately with such discharges. Fortunately, toxic loads, including oil discharges, tend only to kill off the outer layers of the first stages of the R.B.F. The material underneath is exposed as the poisoned layer sloughs off the disc. The new film usually allows full recovery of the plant after the slug of toxic material has passed.

9.3.5 Design loadings

Steels[1] has produced a design procedure for R.B.F.'s based on work by Hartman[2]. It is applicable to populations from 400 up to several thousand. The design has as its principal criteria the relationship between the percentage B.O.D. removal required and the disc area per unit of flow. For any particular percentage removal required for a given strength of influent sewage, a value of the F/q ratio (area of disc/corrected flow) can be calculated. The corrected flow is achieved by multiplying the estimated flow by a factor which takes account of the number of stages used, and a second factor which takes account of the number of people served. See Tables 9.1 and 9.2.

Table 9.1 *(from[1]). Flow correction factors for population equivalents.*

Persons equivalent	q (m^3/min) correction factor
10 000	1
5000 to 10 000	1.1 to 1.2
1500 to 5000	1.2 to 1.3
400 to 1500	1.3 to 1.5
400	1.5

Table 9.2 *(from[1]) Correction of* F *factor for stage numbers greater than two.*

No. of stages	F, *correction factor*
3	0.91
4	0.87
more than 4	0.85

For a purely domestic population of 400, this procedure would be as follows:—

Flow q (uncorrected) = 180 l x 400 l/d, assuming no infiltration, which is unlikely for this population

$$= 72 \text{ m}^3/\text{d} = 0.050 \text{ m}^3/\text{min}.$$

B.O.D. load assuming 0.037 kg B.O.D./cap. day to filter zone

$$= 14.8 \text{ kg/d}.$$

The flow correction factor (from Table 9.1) is 1.5

$$q \text{ (corrected)} = 1.5 \times 0.050 \text{ m}^3/\text{min} = 0.075 \text{ m}^3/\text{min}.$$

$$\text{Influent B.O.D.}_5 = \frac{14.8}{0.072} \text{ mg/l} = 205 \text{ mg/l}.$$

The outlet B.O.D.$_5$ is 20 mg/l (assumed).

% removal of B.O.D. is approximately 90%.

From the curve in Fig. 9.1, the F/q value is approximately 18 000.
Therefore $F = 18\ 000 \times 0.075\ \text{m}^2 = 1350\ \text{m}^2$.
The correction factor for a four stage process would be 0.85 (from Table 9.2)

$$F = 1150\ \text{m}^2.$$

Using 3 m discs this requires 81 discs.
Four stages of 21 discs would give a total area of 1188 m^2.
The hydraulic loading would be 60.6 l/m^2 d and the B.O.D. loading would be 12.5 g B.O.D./m^2 d. A limit of 100 g B.O.D./m^2 d is placed on the first stage. The present design gives a corrected value of 75 g/m^2 d.

A series of checks is built in to the system to avoid overloading. The above rough design procedure gives some indication of the loading figures for satisfactory working.

With smaller scale units, however, the correction factors become of greater importance and the B.O.D.$_5$ loading rate has to be reduced to around 7–8 g B.O.D.$_5$/m^2 d. This is the B.O.D.$_5$ to the R.B.F. and not the overall inlet B.O.D.$_5$. The number of stages used again tends to be increased to five.

Satisfactory results have been obtained in Britain for a wide range of strengths of sewage and flow loadings. For the smaller schemes of approximately 25–50 persons, treating mainly domestic sewage, the R.B.F. can be based on an approximate figure of 6 m^2/cap. of disc area.

9.3.6   Power requirements

The R.B.F. shows considerable savings in running costs over the activated sludge process, since with a well balanced system, the only power required is to rotate the disc; (assuming sufficient head is available). Since the discs are made out of light material, the power requirements are small. The power consumption is a function of the speed of revolution, the power consumed increasing exponentially with speed of rotation. Steels quotes figures of 75 W/m of shaft for 3 m diam. discs at 1 r.p.m. This is equivalent to approximately 2.2 W/disc. Assuming a loading of 7 g B.O.D.$_5$/m^2 d, the energy required per capita would be given by

$$\frac{37}{7} \times \frac{2.2}{14.1}\ \text{W/cap. or } 0.83\ \text{W/cap.}$$

This gives approximately 20 watt hours per capita day, or 7.3 kWh/cap. yr. For smaller communities, this would increase to approximately 20 kWh/cap. yr for 100 persons, and perhaps 40 kWh/cap. yr for very small communities. The power consumption of extended aeration schemes would be around 5–10 times these values. Increasing the speed of rotation achieves a measure of improvement in B.O.D. removal; however, the increase in power consumption is high.

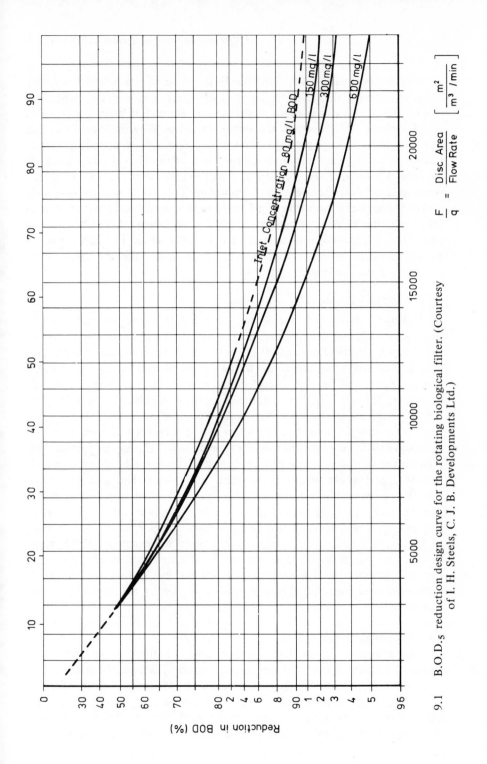

9.1 B.O.D.₅ reduction design curve for the rotating biological filter. (Courtesy of I. H. Steels, C. J. B. Developments Ltd.)

9.3.7   Start-up time

As with the percolating filter, the R.B.F. shows some loss in efficiency with decrease in temperature, due to the onset of winter. Similarly, the build up of film on the discs is slower in the colder months. Maturation times from 4 weeks in the summer to 10 weeks in the winter, should be allowed. Should the discs stop due to electricity cuts, the filter will require a short period of time to recover. If the stoppage is of short duration (two or three hours), little harm will be done. However, if the stoppage is prolonged, the film becomes black and tends to slough off. The film in this condition does not appear to settle well, probably due to the formation of gas bubbles. This usually leads to carry over of solids into the effluent. Whenever possible, arrangements should be made to rotate the disc occasionally to prevent the drying out of the film above the sewage. Oversize motors are often recommended to take the extra torque produced on start-up in such a situation.

9.3.8   Sludge production and settlement

As previously mentioned, the sludge from R.B.F.'s tends by nature to be composed of discrete filamentous material with settlement velocities between 1 and 2 mm/s. Overflow rates of $30-36 \, m^3/m^2 d$ are not uncommon and appear to give good settlement efficiency. In the case of package plants, however, the overflow rate is not the only consideration, as weir length becomes increasingly important. The weir overflow rate, therefore, for such plants should be less than $100 \, m^3/m$ day. The sludge production figures vary considerably. However, the results of a survey carried out at the water pollution research laboratory indicate approximately 0.6 g sludge dry solids produced/gm $B.O.D._5$ applied for the whole primary and secondary sludge. However, most of this would be at approximately 96% M.C. and would occupy considerably less volume than activated sludge. Estimates considerably in excess of these figures are often suggested by R.B.F. manufacturers, e.g. 1 kg sludge/kg $B.O.D._5$ removed, is common, which would give an overall sludge production of 0.05–0.06 kg/cap. d for the R.B.F. stage, with a probable total sludge production in primary settlement and R.B.F. stages of approximately 0.08–0.085 kg/cap. d. The volume is not usually too critical on small plants as desludging is usually carried out three or four times a year. As with other processes, the charge is usually per tanker trip and not per m^3 transported.

9.4   Environmental aspects

A major advantage of the R.B.F. is that noise is reduced to very low levels compared with the activated sludge package plants, which may be audible up to 150 m from the source. The fly nuisance caused by Psychoda and other flies, on percolating filters, is prevented by the regular submergence of the discs. There remain, however, the dangers inherent in any package plant. The torque on the shaft is sufficient to pull a child into the filter. However, the filter is usually housed and the provision of locks on the removable panels should prevent both accidents and unauthorised stoppages.

The head loss through the R.B.F. is only of the order of 10 cm, which allows some flexibility in siting the units. There is little reason, apart from cost considerations, why the R.B.F. cannot be disguised by an outer building shell, or, as in several places, the unit may be sited partly below ground.

9.5 Summary

One problem associated with the use of R.B.F.'s is the relative expense of the system. However, by making the tanks out of different materials, considerable savings can be achieved, as in the case of the Klargester design of the Ames Crosta Biodisc.

The system is similar to the larger Biodisc, using a combined unit of primary settlement, R.B.F. compartment and secondary settlement. The number of discs per stage is less than the Biodisc and they are made out of reinforced plastic, shaped to give added strength to prevent disc to disc contact.

The advantages of the process may be summarized as: low maintenance requirements, the ability to function under conditions of shock loading, low running costs and low noise levels.

References
[1] I. H. STEELS, Design basis for the rotating disc process, *J. Effluent Wat. Treat.* **4**, 1974, 431–445.
[2] H. HARTMAN, Der tanchtropfkörper, *Osterr. Wasserw.*, **17**, 1965, 264–269.

Suggested further reading
[1] K. V. ELLIS and S. E. I. BANAGA, A study of rotating disc treatment units operating at different temperatures, *Water Pollut. Control* 1976, 73–92.

10 Sludge production and disposal

10.1 Introduction

In 1972 Gale[1] estimated that the total amount of sludges produced yearly in Britain was approximately 1 million tonnes dry solids and cost approximately £10 per tonne for treatment and disposal. Assuming a daily per capita production of 0.075 kg suspended solids for a population of 60 million, with a primary settlement removal efficiency of 70%, the primary sludge production totals 3.15 Gg of solids which, at an average moisture content of 97%, would occupy 105 000 m^3. When the nature of the sludge is considered, the immensity of the problem from physical, aesthetic and sanitary viewpoints becomes obvious.

Unfortunately, it does not appear to be possible to produce an economic sewage treatment process which does not produce sludge. It is, however, still possible to find manufacturers of plant, and others, who maintain that this is not so. The following discussion is not intended to be rigorous in its approach, but it is hoped that it will show why the production of sludge in all the processes used in small works must be a result of the process itself.

10.1.1 Cesspools and primary settlement tanks

Cesspools are merely containers which store sewage until it may be conveniently removed, usually to a centralized treatment and disposal depot. The retention period in the cesspool is insufficient to allow a build up of organisms capable of digesting the solids. The cesspool must be impervious, hence the solids cannot seep away. The presence of solids in this case is obvious.

Primary settlement tanks allow settlement of solids and are usually designed in small works to allow a few days' accumulation of the deposited solids (see Chapter 7). Digestion of the solids would ruin the efficiency of the tanks by producing rising sludges which would eventually pass over the outlet weir. The build up of organisms which could cause digestion is prevented by regular tank desludging and cleaning.

Both the above processes must result in the production of sludges which are very little different from the original input material.

10.1.2 Septic tanks and Imhoff tanks

These are dealt with in more detail in Chapter 6. In both cases, solids settle to form a sludge which then digests. Imhoff tanks are only commonly met with at small sewage works in Britain, as part of a unit, e.g. the Ames Crosta Biodisc primary settlement stage acts in a similar manner to an Imhoff tank. The tanks are usually desludged at intervals of less than 4 months and under British climatic conditions digestion of solids is probably less than that found in most septic tanks which should be desludged every nine to twelve months. Septic tanks operate as cold sludge digesters and in this context it is interesting to note that in 1973, of 9 heated (32°C) digesters under the control of the Greater London Council, none showed more than 50% reduction of organic matter, the average being 44% reduction. Since the average organic content of the sludges was 78%, this is equivalent to an average digestion of approximately one third of the sludge solids. This probably represents the maximum achievable digestion and is rarely achieved in septic tanks. In addition, many septic tanks are desludged too enthusiastically with sludge, liquor and scum being totally removed. Under these latter circumstances, very low digestion rates are to be expected.

10.1.3   *Activated sludge units and percolating filters*

The activated sludge process in its usual small scale extended aeration form has suffered badly from poor design which leads to excessive discharge of solids with the effluent. Such works may appear to be producing little sludge, since most of it will undergo regular hydraulic wash out.

Two processes occur in an activated sludge unit which can be simply written as:—

activated sludge floc + organic material = oxidized organic matter and energy. The released energy is used by bacteria as follows:

energy + bacterial floc and organic substrate = new cellular material.

In addition, the bacteria break down to produce material which can be re-used by other bacteria plus unusable material. The mass of sludge solids produced per mass of B.O.D. removed is given the designation 'a'. In conventional plants, approximately 0.55 kg sludge dry solids are produced per kg B.O.D. removed. If new sludge were not produced, the mixed liquor sludge concentration would be reduced and the process would fail.

Unfortunately, as described in Chapter 8, the sludge concentration in package plants can increase to a relatively high M.L.S.S. concentration of perhaps 9000 mg/l over a period of several weeks. An underloaded sludge is produced which becomes increasingly difficult to settle in the final settlement unit. This situation is often aggravated by overaeration and large hydraulic surges. The sludge then disappears over the outlet weir. A very low M.L.S.S. concentration results, and the cycle starts afresh (see Fig. 4.2 and Chapter 4). Overaeration alone can often lead to a light coloured pin head sludge which is very difficult to settle and will be lost over the outlet weir. The net result in either case will be a plant which never requires desludging. The drawback to operating a plant in this way is that the effluent will be poor. This may lead to problems with the statutory authority dealing with river pollution, and possibly to closure of the site, school, etc.

Although the percolating filter process and the rotating biological filters are somewhat more difficult to treat from a theoretical viewpoint, since they consist of very many different types of organisms, each occupying its own particular locality in the filter, nevertheless the processes of adsorption, breakdown, cellular growth and grazing by higher organisms all within the filter, ensure that sludge is produced.

The process of aerobic digestion which is becoming increasingly favoured, will be discussed later in this chapter. However, here again a limit exists to the breakdown of organic sludges.

10.2   Sludge types
Several different types of sludges can be distinguished in sewage treatment processes. The origin of the sludge affects not only the physical characteristics such as their ability to be pumped, but also their sanitary and odiferous qualities.

10.2.1   Detritus sludge
This is not usually found in small scale works, since it consists of the settled inorganic material usually separated out in grit traps, channels or various proprietary devices. It should contain less than 15% organic matter and can be washed and used for a variety of purposes. If well washed, it can be used for landfill or can be buried with little chance of nuisance being caused. A certain amount of screenings containing rags, fat balls etc. are produced at small works. The use of screens prior to the inlet of an activated sludge unit is a contentious subject. However, little appears to be gained from this approach; the use of screens on the outlet of the activated sludge zone appears to work equally well.

10.2.2   Primary sludges
These consist of inorganic detritus, silt, animal and vegetable fibres, oil and grease (mineral and vegetable). They are contaminated by faecal matter and should be treated as a potential health hazard. The amount of sludge produced in the primary tanks will depend on many factors including the design of the tanks, the temperature of the incoming liquid, the rate of flow and the solids concentration. On large scale works, samples of the primary settlement tanks inlet and outlet streams may be taken and suspended solids deposition calculated.

Septic tank sludges and Imhoff tank sludges not only digest but also consolidate, sometimes to very high solids contents; e.g. greater than 20% solids is not uncommon. At such a high solids concentration, the friction factors for pumping this material become very high. However, for a septic tank partially desludged at nine monthly intervals, the sludge solids concentration should not be much greater than 10%. The sludge production from septic tanks is discussed in detail in Chapter 6.

Primary settlement tank sludges and their rate of production are described in detail in Chapter 7, and need little further description. Since both primary settlement sludges and septic tank sludges are contaminated by faecal material, both must be treated as a potential health hazard. Their treatment and disposal is discussed later in this chapter.

10.2.3 Secondary sludges

The production of secondary sludges is discussed in Chapter 8, Section 8.2.5.

The sludge removed would be flocculent, brown to dark brown in colour with a damp, earthy small. The organic content would be high, e.g. 77%, and it would be very difficult to consolidate it to much beyond 99% M.C. It is characteristically difficult to dewater, although, since it is not as noxious as primary sludge, it can be spread on land except where heavy metals are discharged from industries into the sewage. In this latter case, the sludge adsorbs many metal ions.

An alternative to the process in which large amounts of settled sludge are abstracted at long intervals is the procedure used, for example, in the Inka separate digestion system, where the small amounts of settled sludge are pumped at regular intervals into a holding tank where the solids undergo aerobic digestion. Air is bubbled through the sludge and the solids can be reduced by approximately 30% over 10–15 days. Further aeration produces a lessening reduction of solids. The principle of small volume abstractions of M.L.S.S. thus ensuring a steady operating condition has already been discussed. However, the use of aerobic digestion has certain advantages as a storage system. The process has, however, suffered to a certain extent from over-optimistic claims suggesting that the sludge would eventually disappear, given sufficient aeration time. High rate sludges will give very high percentage breakdowns on aeration. However, most extended aeration sludges are already well stabilized. Blending of the sludges has been suggested; however, this is not generally used in practice. The sludge concentration with time of digestion is shown in Fig. 10.1 which indicates the logarithmic reduction in breakdown efficiency with time. Sufficient air must be passed through the liquor to keep the solids in suspension.

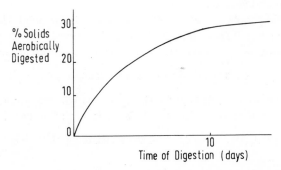

10.1   Aerobic digestion of activated sludge solids.

Ames Crosta suggest a figure of approximately 1 kg oxygenation capacity per kg organic matter applied. This latter figure is equivalent to 1.3 kg M.L.S.S. applied. The sludge produced in the aerobic digester is well stabilized and may be transferred to land for disposal. However, it can be re-used in the aeration compartment or may be used to seed a new plant. This is particularly useful in cases where part of the activated sludge plant may be shut down for a time, e.g. at a camping site during the non-peak periods. The sludge does not acclimatize immediately; however, after being returned for 24 hours, it regains its former bioxidation ability.

Humus sludge from a conventional percolating filter is a watery, browny-grey coloured suspension which is often pumped back to the primary settlement tanks on larger works. In smaller works, the sludge is allowed to remain in the humus tank for periods up to 5 to 7 days, when the sludge can achieve 96% M.C. The amount of sludge produced varies greatly throughout the year, being greatest in the spring when more film sloughs off the filter. However, a general figure of between 0.025–0.030 kg/cap. d can be used for most purposes.

The rotating biological filters have similarities with percolating filters and again produce amounts of sludge which must be settled in order to obtain a clarified effluent. This may be achieved by an *in situ* settlement chamber as in the Biodisc process, or by a separate settlement tank.

Fortunately, the material from the R.B.F. tends to be filamentous in nature and consequently possesses a high settlement velocity. Moisture contents of 95–96% are possible for the secondary sludge.

10.3   The effect of sludge moisture content

In most large scale works, some form of sludge treatment is adopted prior to disposal. The treatment is intended both to reduce the volume of the sludge and to render it less noxious or dangerous. All sewage sludges are difficult to dewater and contain large amounts of liquid associated with very small amounts of solid material. A settled activated sludge of 8000 mg/l is only 0.8% solids. A spadable sludge may still retain greater than 75% moisture. The influence of the moisture content on the volume of sludge is extremely large, as the following sample calculation indicates.

Assume 2000 people are served by an activated sludge plant which produces sludge at the rate of 0.55 kg S.S. per kg B.O.D. removed. If there is no primary settlement, then a per capita B.O.D. input of 0.0555 kg/d would produce:

$$0.55 \times 2000 \times 0.0555 \text{ kg new sludge/d, i.e. 61 kg/d.}$$

If the dry sludge solids density is 1400 kg/m^3, and ignoring mixing effects, we can consider the sludge to consist of two fractions: one solid, one liquid,

i.e. at 99.0% M.C. the 61 kg dry S.S. are associated with 99 x 61 kg liquid,

or in volume terms:

$$\frac{61}{1400} \text{ m}^3 \text{ sludge is associated with } \frac{99 \times 61}{1000} \text{ m}^3 \text{ liquid}$$

giving a total volume of 6.08 m^3.

If we could consolidate the sludge to 98% M.C., the same volume of sludge would now be associated with

$$\frac{98 \times 61 \text{ m}^3}{2000} \text{ liquid. This would give a total volume of 3.03 m}^3.$$

A general expression can be stated that:

$$\frac{\text{Volume of sludge at M.C. [1]}}{\text{Volume of sludge at M.C. [2]}} = \frac{100 - \text{M.C. [2]}}{100 - \text{M.C. [1]}}$$

An example of how the volume of 1 m^3 of sludge varies with M.C. is given in Table 10.1.

Table 10.1 *Effect of moisture content on sludge volume.*

M.C. %	Volume
99.75	1 m^3
99.50	0.5 m^3
99.00	0.25 m^3
98.00	0.125 m^3
96.00	0.0625 m^3
92.00	0.03125 m^3

Although this calculation procedure becomes increasingly less accurate for M.C.'s less than 80%, it does indicate the importance of sludge thickening. In many small schemes, less than one tanker load may be transported each trip, and the effects of high moisture contents are not necessarily significant since the charge will usually be per trip and not per cubic metre.

10.4   Sludge conditioning
The more common methods of conditioning are described below in order to help the reader to converse with local authorities' district engineers etc. about final disposal problems. However, most of these methods are not satisfactory for use in small communities.

Elutriation is the stirring of sludge with approximately 2–3 times its own volume of final effluent and allowing the sludge to settle. The percentage of fine materials is reduced, as also are the concentration of ammonia compounds and the sludge alkalinity. The main advantage of this method lies in the reduced coagulant dose requirement of elutriated sludges prior to further treatment.

The addition of aluminium and/or iron compounds in solution reduces the electrostatic repulsive forces between sludge particles, thus allowing the particles to agglomerate. The process is further helped by the floc formation of the iron or aluminium hydroxides which form a scavenging, easily settleable sludge. This is usually referred to as 'coagulation', the added salt being a coagulant.

A modern process which acts in a somewhat different manner uses polyelectrolytes to form a flocculated easier draining sludge structure. Polyelectrolytes are high molecular weight compounds which may be positively or negatively charged. The cationic (positively charged) polymers are the most useful for sludge conditioning.

10.5   Sludge treatment

Treatment methods for sludges can take many different forms. However, the following includes those most likely to be met with. Mesophilic digestion is a heated anaerobic process basically similar but more efficient than the digestion process occurring in a septic tank (see Chapter 6). This process can be inexpensive due to the production of methane gas which may not only heat the digester but produce excess gas to run dual fuel engines. In many instances, sludges collected from small works by local authorities are digested with works sludge. The digested sludge is less noxious than before, contains less grease and is safe to be used for land spreading on fallow land. Cattle may be allowed to graze the field after 3 to 4 weeks where the sludge has been discharged at rates of 70 to 150 m^3/hectare.

Vacuum filtration is usually performed on a rotating drum. The sludge, after conditioning with either inorganic coagulants or polyelectrolytes, is dewatered by vacuum filtration, using one of a number of different filter media, to a moisture content of approximately 75—80%. Pressure filtration can also be used. This is a batch fed horizontal ram applied pressure filter bed operating at pressures of 280 to 560 kN/m^2. Conditioning, using inorganic coagulant plus lime, is usual, and the filter medium is terylene or other synthetic cloth. The cake moisture content is usually taken to 60—65% M.C. Air drying followed by tipping is common. The lime helps to reduce rodent infestation and smell.

A newer method which was in disfavour until recently is centrifugation after conditioning with a polyelectrolyte. Although well used in Scandinavian countries, it is only recently gaining favour in Britain. It is usual to quote two operating parameters for centrifuges; namely, solids content in the cake (approximately 23% solids or 77% M.C.) and solids recovery which may be between 95 and 99%. The centrate (clarified liquor) may have 1000—2000 mg/l S.S. and must be treated before discharge. Work carried out at Dumfries using a centrifuge to dewater septic tank and other sludges has been reported by the Scottish Development Department [2].

Various sludge concentrators are available; mainly operating on the principle of gravity dewatering prior to belt pressing. In one type of concentrator, the sludge forms a rolling plug in a rotating dewatering frame. As the plug flattens, parings are fed to a belt press. Some form of fibrous material may be required with weak sludges, to aid plug formation.

The Satec sludge concentrator is of particular interest as it can be mounted on a low loader for transportation. Such a system is used by Inverness County Council. After polymer addition, the sludge is flocculated for a short period before being fed to a belt filter where it dewaters under gravity. A second belt filters the sludge under pressure to a final moisture content of approximately 92% for an activated sludge, and 84% for a primary, or mixed primary and septic, sludge. An estimate of the costs of hiring the sludge concentrator from Inverness County Council, now part of the Highland Regional Council, would be £6–10 per hour. This, however, is an estimate, since the machine is not normally used for isolated small sites. Assuming adequate water and electricity supplies were available, a trip of 30 miles with half a day's sludge pressing would take almost one complete day.

10.6 Disposal of sludges

Three methods are commonly used for almost all small scale works sludge disposal:

a) tankering by local authorities or others;
b) land disposal:
c) drying beds.

10.6.1 Tankering

For a small camp site, motel etc., this is by far the best method of sludge disposal and, considering that no expense apart from fees and the cost of hard standing is involved, it could be cheaper than drying beds.

The requirement of local authorities or regional authorities to collect and dispose of septic tank sludge is vested in Acts of Parliament. However, since a mandatory requirement on the authority to empty septic tanks from communities not served by public sewers would be very expensive, the authorities concerned were allowed to choose whether to accept this burden. Therefore, in Scotland for example, some regions do collect septic tank sludge under the drainage rate, without charge, whereas others charge for this service. A further complication is that farms and trade effluent sludges may be removed but a charge will be made for this service. Unfortunately, the Acts concerned, e.g. the Sewerage (Scotland) Act 1968, do not appear to have dealt with activated sludge schemes.

The charges levied for desludging vary considerably, e.g. £30 per trip from a disposal firm, to as little as £3 per hour + V.A.T. from a Regional Council. At the time of going to press, an average price in Scotland would be approximately £5–10 per hour (1976); travelling time would be included at this rate.

10.6.2 Land disposal

This method involves the spraying of sludges onto land or the burying of more noxious sludges in trenches which are then covered. Primary or mixed primary and septic tank sludges, should not be applied to land directly without some form of treatment. Primary sludges, in particular, contain large amounts of grease which make them a nuisance, and their organic content can lead to rodent infestation. In addition, the breakdown of the primary sludge can lead to 'sewage sickness', possibly caused by the breakdown of the grease. The possibility of transference of disease, the smell nuisance and the deleterious effect on the soil can be reduced by liming the sludge and ensuring complete burial. However, this method of sludge disposal is not recommended for primary septic tank and Imhoff type sludges.

Activated sludges and, in particular, the well stabilized sludges produced from an aerobic digester produce less problems since they are well oxidized. It is preferable to plough in the material after spraying on the land, in order to reduce smell nuisances.

10.6.3   Drying beds

These are usually rectangular beds with brick or concrete walls, having a series of underdrains arranged in a herring-bone pattern. The bed itself is composed of a free draining material often having 250 mm of 25–40 mm diam. clinker as base with 10–15 mm of finer 6–12 mm diam. material as a surface dressing. As some of the surface layer is inevitably removed when the sludge is lifted, make-up material is required. Raking of the surface after sludge lifting is advisable, and forking gently at long intervals may help. This should be carried out by men standing on planks laid on the bed to prevent bed consolidation. The actual drying period in Britain varies considerably over the country since the sludge loses moisture mainly by evaporation, after an initial drainage period. For this reason, the flow of air across the top of the beds should be unobstructed. Unfortunately, since this is one of the least aesthetic parts of a small works, it tends to be allocated to the low lying ground at the site perimeter, with deciduous trees close by. The resulting poor air flow and the problems of leaf fall and seeding can completely ruin the efficiency of the drying bed. The difficulties then lead to serious neglect and rank weeds proliferate. The liquor from the drying beds is high in S.S. and must be returned to the inlet of the sewage works. The sludge on small works is wasted in small amounts and it is usually only necessary to build one drying bed sectioned by planks, turf etc. in order to fill one section at a time to a depth of 200–300 mm. Standing water which accumulates after a few days can be decanted by removing turf or planks etc. After drying, which may take several months during the winter, the sludge is lifted with broad tined forks, together with the top few millimetres of clinker and can be used for land fill. The fine clinker surface should be topped up occasionally. Primary sludges again produce problems of rodent infestation. The present sizing calculations have greatly increased the area required to approximately 0.75 m^3 area per person served for the types of sludges produced from small scale works. On larger works, the use of sludge consolidation tanks can reduce the bed area required. However, the extra expense and labour are not worthwhile on the plants covered in this book. On a solids/area basis, a design figure would be approximately 11 kg solids/m^2 for digested sludges. It should be stressed that drying beds require considerable labour and they tend to suffer neglect at small works due to the unaesthetic nature of the material. Most large sewage works are looking to mechanical methods of sludge lifting, in part, because of the difficulty of employing labour for this job. Whilst drying beds can be used on small works, their use should only be countenanced after ascertaining that labour availability is likely to continue over the life of the drying bed.

References

[1] R. S. GALE, The sludge treatment and disposal problem, *Symposium on Incineration of Refuse and Sludge*, University of Southampton, Jan. 1972. Water Pollution Research Laboratory Reprint 661.

[2] Scottish Development Dept., Engineering Division, Applied research and development, Report No. A.R.D.I. June 1974.

11 Tertiary treatment

11.1 The need for tertiary treatment

Tertiary treatment or polishing of effluent has become increasingly important as the River or Water Authorities have attempted to improve the state of rivers and lakes. Usually the method is chosen to improve an effluent which is already to Royal Commission standards. In the case of small scale sewage treatment schemes, we are concerned mainly with trying to compensate for the inevitable difficulties of secondary treatment by percolating filters or activated sludge processes. It should be stressed that the use of tertiary treatment processes is unsuitable for effluents which are the result of poor secondary treatment operation.

Tertiary treatment was recommended by the Ministry in their 1969 memorandum[1] after surveys had shown that many small extended aeration plants were producing poor quality effluents[2]. The major reasons for such poor quality have been stressed in earlier chapters. It is, however, possible to produce effluents to 20 : 30 standard or better with conventional activated sludge or extended aeration schemes, provided they are operated in a suitable manner.

Small percolating filter schemes as described in CP 302: 1972 do not conform to the usual practice adopted by large works since the humus tank settlement is not recommended for small populations. The use of some tertiary treatment stage for such schemes is mandatory since effluents from the primary filter would be unlikely to be better than 40–70 mg/l S.S. with wide variations being found throughout the year.

11.2 Tertiary treatment and suspended solids

Both percolating filters and activated sludge schemes will produce some waste material which will not settle well. If a humus tank is not present, a percolating filter effluent will contain filamentous material which must be removed. Because of its biological origin, the suspended solids in the effluent have a considerable B.O.D., a plot of S.S. against B.O.D. very often being linear. The removal of S.S. alone will therefore remove quite a large percentage of the effluent B.O.D.

Tertiary treatment methods may simply remove S.S. as in the case of microstrainers, upward flow clarifiers and rapid gravity sand filters. Alternatively, some biological treatment may occur as in lagoons. A further alternative is grass plots where some infiltration occurs as well as S.S. removal. Percolation of effluent into the subsoil requires the consent of the river boards or water

100

authority and is dealt with adequately in CP 302. Sewage contains a considerable amount of nitrogen which may be present as nitrate. The presence of this conservative ion in a water supply may render it unfit for consumption. In addition, there exists the possibility of bacterial and virus infestation of underground aquifers. Unfortunately, those situations where ground disposal is most likely to be used, i.e. a very small population living above porous strata in an isolated situation, are those most likely to be served by aquifer or well water. It is necessary in these circumstances to carry the effluent some considerable distance, e.g. 50 m away from the well in the direction of flow, prior to subsoil disposal.

11.3   Treatment methods

11.3.1   Grass plots

Grass plots are probably the most economical method of effluent polishing; however, they are by no means always successful. In essence, a plot of land is divided into three sections and graded to a slope between 1 : 80 and 1 : 100. Effluent may be sprayed onto the land or, more simply, discharged evenly from a channel which may be concrete or tile onto a paved area to prevent erosion. After percolating downhill, it is collected in a further channel. The grass tends to grow rapidly and must be cut at regular intervals to a height of approximately 5 cms. Many literature sources quote per capita area requirements for schemes where humus tanks are present, consequently areas tend to be low. Areas from 2–3 persons per m^2 area are quoted. Allowing for three alternately used plots, this gives approximately 1 m^2 per person. Since large S.S. concentrations and variable flows will be experienced at small works it is necessary to allow at least 3 m^2/person. There is no necessity to seed with a particular strain of grass, and removal of accumulated solids after several years can be achieved by scraping and regrading during the spring or summer. The use of three plots allows some leeway in grass cutting times which is important in small scale works. The cuttings are best removed from the plots.

In practice the plots can remove up to three quarters of the suspended solids together with half the applied B.O.D. The channels must be kept clean and the presence of rank weeds discouraged by cutting. Channelling is usually caused by too great a slope causing erosion and should be prevented by regrading.

Although the method is simple, it has considerable problems. In a recent discussion on the merits of grass plots, opinions were wide-ranging, their use being recommended by those accustomed to low rainfall and porous soils, whilst those more used to heavy soils and high rainfall denigrated their application. One problem in areas of high humidity is the breeding of mosquitos on grass plots. However, provided the soil is of a coarse, porous nature and if the works is in an area with a rainfall which is moderate, the use of grass plots when well maintained will give satisfactory effluents and should be investigated first.

11.3.2   Clarifiers

The use of upward flow clarifiers to produce a satisfactory effluent is common even though the costs are considerable. A typical installation is shown in Fig. 15.6. The cost of such an installation for a population equivalent of 250 could be £2000 with approximately £150 for civil works. In essence the tank acts as a secondary settlement tank with a coarse upward flow filter medium at the outlet. The head loss through the units is often less than 10 cms with maximum overflow rates between 0.8 and 0.9 m^3/m^2 bed h at maximum flow. Satisfactory beds have been made of overlapping expanded wire mesh; however, a more usual medium is pea gravel of 4–6 mm diam. in a 150 mm deep bed. Deeper and finer beds provide more efficient removal but are difficult to clean efficiently. The beds have often been made with their surface too close to the T.W.L. leading to carry over of solids. The figure of 300 mm given in CP 302: 1972 takes account of hydraulic variations and is usually followed by manufacturers. The solids are not strained by the media, since the interstices are often of the order of several thousand μm, whereas the S.S. themselves from, say, an extended aeration plant may be less than 100 μm. The process probably works by allowing coagulation and settlement in the bed itself.

The tank in which the bed sits may be the secondary settlement tank in the case of a percolating filter. Some sludge will accumulate at the bottom of the tank and should be returned at not greater than weekly intervals to the primary or septic tank by pumping. Weirs and the necessary scumboards should be brushed daily if possible, and the media backwashed at intervals of 1 to 2 weeks after lowering the tank T.W.L.

The removal efficiency for a well designed clarifier should be approximately 60% S.S. with a B.O.D. removal of approximately 35%. The man hours of maintenance required are probably twice those of grass plots. The main advantage of such clarifiers is the very small land requirements. Examples of sizes quoted by Satec are, for a population equivalent of 880 people: the dimensions are 2.74 m x 2.74 m.

11.3.3   Microstrainers

Microstrainers, as the name implies, consist of woven mesh of stainless steel with tens of thousands of apertures per cm^2. It is supported on a bronze frame; one end is open to allow the ingress of effluent, the liquid passing laterally through the sides of the drum under a small hydraulic head which builds up to approximately 150 mms. Although the microstrainer is continuously washed by a jet of water impinging on the top of the rotating drum, when treating effluent a U.V. light is necessary to reduce growth on the media. Although microstrainers are efficient in removal of S.S., they are not commonly used for the type of installations described in this book.

11.3.4   Sand filtration

Slow sand filters are commonly used at large works to polish effluents. Rapid gravity filters use a greater flow rate; however, they require back-washing with high flow rates and air scour every few days. The latter is unsatisfactory for a small sewage works, due to the labour involved. Slow sand filters consist of a layer of fine sand approximately 450 mm deep overlying pea gravel. The pea gravel should be 20–30 mm although in the past 3/8 in or 10 mm diam. gravel was used successfully. The depth of pea gravel should be between 200 and 300 mm. A depth of 8 in or 200 mm has often been used. The flow to the filter of $0.15 \text{ m}^3/\text{m}^2$ h quoted in CP 302: 1972 should be taken as a maximum which is applicable to the treatment of humus tank effluent. Should a sand filter be used without the humus tank, the flow should be reduced to an average value of $0.05 \text{ m}^3/\text{m}^2$ h. However, it is unlikely that a sand filter would be considered for the small populations (<100) not using a humus tank. The head loss through the filter increases with use up to a maximum effluent depth on the bed limited by the wall depth. Depths of 1 to 1.25 ft (300 to 380 mm) are usually used. In practice, two or more beds are used, the flow being switched at convenient times, usually once or twice fortnightly. After draining, the top few mm of accumulated sludge and sand is removed. After several scrapings, the bed surface must be replenished with clean sand so that the sand layer does not become less than approximately 300 mm (one foot). The scrapped sand can be washed and settled while the scum is returned to the works inlet. Removal efficiencies of over 50% S.S. and 35% B.O.D. can be regularly achieved with reasonable care.

11.3.5 Lagoons

Lagoons can be used for the treatment of sewage effluent; however, they have an unenviable reputation, somewhat undeserved, of being odorous and the cause of fly nuisance. Essentially they provide a long retention time during which the solids settle out. A complex process involving the growth of photosynthetic plants and the solubilization of settled solids occurs during which nitrogen bubbles may cause lifting of sludge to the surface. For this reason the most efficient lagoons consist of interconnected bays with a scum board at the outlet. With retention times of several days, the surface areas can be as high as $1 \text{ m}^2/\text{cap.}$ unless deep lagoons (>1 m deep) are used. The removal of S.S. is often poor, being less than 40% although a multiple pond system can remove up to 60% S.S. Since the process does not work purely by removing suspended solids, the B.O.D. removal is nearly as high as the S.S. removal. In general, unless land is available readily in an area which is unlikely to attract children or give rise to odour nuisance, the use of lagoons is to be avoided.

11.4 Summary

With very small sewage works, one of the major problems is the variability of loading experienced both diurnally and annually. Additionally, there will invariably be occasions when small works will produce poor effluents which will require to be treated by the tertiary treatment stage. Finally, the system used must operate within the stringent requirements of the yearly climatology.

Microstrainers have advantages due to their high throughput rate; however, they require to be taken out of commission at regular intervals (6 monthly) for maintenance. The provision of duplicate facilities appears to be too expensive for small works.

The use of grass plots is attractive with the right soil conditions; they will work well unless severe icing occurs; the labour required is not excessive and is not demanding. They do not work well in heavy soils.

The use of upward flow clarifiers involves more labour and, since pumping is involved, it can be regarded as more skilful work. Provided it is designed for the maximum flow, it will stand short hydraulic surges.

References

[1] *Technical Memorandum on Activated Sludge Sewage Treatment Installations Providing for a Long Period of Aeration*, Min. Housing and Local Government, H.M.S.O., London, 1969.

[2] A. L. DOWNING, G. A. TRUESDALE, and A. E. BIRKBECK, Some observations on the performance of extended aeration plants, *Survr. munic. Cty. Engr.*, 12 Sept., 1964, 29–34A.

Suggested further reading

M. R. V. DAVISS, Treatment of humus tank effluent on grass plots, *Survr. Munic. Cty. Engr.*, 8th June, 1957, 613–614.

12 Structural design and construction

12.1 Introduction

12.1.1 Special requirements for sewage works

Current practice in the use of concrete for civil engineering structures is to design according to the various limit states as defined in CP 110: 1972[1]. These limit states fall into two groups. The first group comprises the failure limit states of ultimate strength and stability of the structure. In this category the structure is designed so that it will not collapse under the action of some predetermined load which will provide an adequate factor of safety in the normal working loads. The second group of limit states consits of the serviceability limit states in which the behaviour of the structure at working load is determined. In this case, limits are put on such factors as the maximum deflections of the structure, the amount of cracking of the concrete, the response to vibrations, the durability of the concrete, etc.

In most types of structures, the failure limit states are of primary importance and the serviceability states are considered of secondary importance if they are checked at all. It is often the case that the satisfaction of the failure limit states will of itself satisfy the serviceability states.

For structures in sewage works, it is obvious that the failure states must be satisfied, but some of the serviceability states are of equal importance. In this type of structure, as would be the case in any liquid retaining structure, the criteria of cracking, durability and permeability are extremely important, and it is not uncommon to find that, in order to satisfy these alternative limit states, the structure is overdesigned with respect to strength. This would be particularly true of small structures.

12.1.2 Structural types

In a typical sewage works four basic types of structures are encountered, each involving different design considerations. These four types are

    a) conduits and interconnecting pipework.
    b) water or liquid retaining structures.
    c) machine and equipment foundations.
    d) protective housings and storage buildings.

In a small sewage plant, the problem is, in some ways, a little simpler. There are two fundamental alternatives in the design of such a plant. Firstly, a small prefabricated package treatment plant could be chosen. The design and details of these plants are given in Chapters 8, 9 and 15, and the only structural problem to be dealt with is that of designing the foundation slab to carry the plant. The second solution is to choose a small *in situ* concrete plant. The structural types encountered in this case are normally only a) and b) above. Any other structure will be of such a small nature that its design would present no difficulty.

The design of conduits and interconnecting pipework is governed by code of practice CP 2005: 1968[2]. This code sets out the problems involved in this type of work, such as the loading on buried pipe lines from the soil above and from any traffic crossing the pipe and possible settlement. In the scale of works dealt with in this book, it would normally be possible to use small diameter flexible pipes and, as long as sufficient cover of soil is provided, no problems should be encountered.

The design of water retaining structures is covered by code of practice CP 2007: 1960[3] and the rest of this chapter will be devoted to this.

12.1.3   Materials

Apart from the obvious requirement of strength, any material used in the construction of sewage works, particularly where it is in contact with liquids, should have additional properties. The material should be impermeable so that any bacterial or chemical pollution of water supply or the environment is prevented. The material should be able to resist the action of any naturally occurring or commonly used chemicals. The material must also be capable of being made in such a way that the surfaces are smooth and well formed to minimize the resistance to flow. Concrete is a particularly suitable material. Provided that the concrete is properly designed and manufactured, it is highly impermeable and, with one notable exception, extremely resistant to chemical attack. The exception to this resistance is the danger of sulphate attack on the concrete and this will be considered later.

Because of the stringent service requirements for sewage works, it is essential that design is undertaken with great care. Because the quality of concrete is so

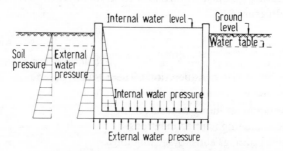

12.1   Cross-section through a tank.

important, equal care should be taken throughout the construction to maintain high quality control and to obtain a well compacted and well cured concrete.

The permeability and chemical resistance of concrete can be improved by the addition of an air entraining agent when the concrete is mixed.

In the case of small tanks, it is impractical and uneconomical to build the tanks of reinforced concrete. Brickwork or blockwork should be considered as an alternative. The bricks used must be of engineering quality and the mortar should be at least a mix of the proportions 1 : 3 for cement : sand. In addition to this, it will be necessary to waterproof the inside of the tank, either by asphalt tanking or by a waterproof cement rendering.

12.2   Analysis and design of water retaining structures

12.2.1   Design loading
The design loads in water retaining structures are, in general, more easily determined than for most structures. Apart from the self weight of the structure, there are two main sources of loading. First, there is the loading arising from the liquid retained, either as a weight of water acting on the base or as a hydrostatic pressure acting on the walls of the tank. These loads can be determined accurately since they are functions only of the physical properties of the liquid and the depth of the tank, both of which are known exactly. The second source of loading is due to the external pressures on the tank due to the surrounding soil and the water in the soil. These will only occur if the tank is at least partially below ground level and are more difficult to ascertain, since they depend on the properties of the soil and a knowledge of the depth of the water table. This information, together with information on the allowable bearing pressure of the foundations on the soil can only be found from some form of site investigation.

Fig. 12.1 shows diagrammatically a cross-section through a tank and the loading for which the tank would have to be designed.

In some cases there may be, in addition to these loads mentioned above, some live loading due to other sources such as machines, but normally these would be small compared to those already considered.

12.2.2   Analysis

General   The moment and forces caused by the loadings shown in Fig. 12.1 will depend on the plan shape of the tank, but whatever the shape, it is clear that alternative loading arrangements must be considered in order to determine the worst possible conditions to be resisted. For example, the forces and moments produced when the tank is full and the water table in the surrounding soil is low could be very different from those produced when the tank is empty and the surrounding water table is high.

Flotation   The situation where the tank is empty and the surrounding water table is high can cause a situation to develop which can result in serious damage, even though the allowable stresses are not exceeded. In circumstances such as these, the tank can actually float due to the excessive external hydrostatic pressure and the low weight of the structure. It has been known for tanks to rise by several feet due to flotation and the damage which this can cause to the connecting pipework and to the tank itself when it sinks again can be very serious. Flotation can be prevented in several ways. Pressure relief valves can be installed in the base which would open, either manually or automatically, when the water pressure under the base reached some predetermined level. This would cause the tank to flood and the additional weight of water in the tank would be enough to stop flotation. An alternative solution would be to extend the base of the tank beyond the walls as shown in Fig. 12.2. When the soil is replaced, the weight of the soil on the top of this toe would provide additional weight to hold the tank down.

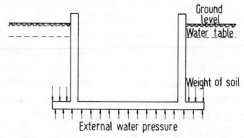

Ground level

Water table.

Weight of soil

External water pressure

12.2   Cross-Section of tank with extended base slab.

Foundation design   One of the major sources of cracking in any structure is differential settlement, and it is important that consideration be given to this problem. Normally, sewage works tend to be in low lying land, perhaps beside a river, so that as much of the flow as possible is by gravity and pumping is kept to a minimum. This often means that the sub-soil in the area of the works is of low strength and waterlogged. An attempt should be made to determine the bearing capacity of the soil and the foundation designed to minimise, or even preclude, the possibility of differential settlement.

As could be expected, the smaller the structure, the less likely is the possibility of differential settlement. But it should be considered even if it is only to come to the conclusion that it can be neglected. This is also true of prefabricated plant, not so much from the point of view of possible damage to the plant, but more from the possibility that differential settlement could cause tilting of the plant with all the consequences that that could bring.

Analyses of circular tanks   When a circular tank is full of liquid, the main force produced in the walls of the tank is the direct tensile force caused by the

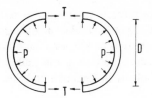

12.3   Forces on a circular tank.

hydrostatic pressure of the liquid. This force acts horizontally in a circumferential direction as is shown in Fig. 12.3.

If the hydrostatic pressure at a depth h is p, then p is given by

$$p = \gamma h$$

where γ is the density of the retained liquid.
The circumferential tensile force T, at this level is given by

$$T = \frac{pD}{2} = \frac{\gamma h D}{2}$$

where D is the diameter of the tank.

Since the tensile force is proportional to the hydrostatic pressure which in turn is proportional to the depth of the liquid, it would appear that the most critical section for design purposes would be at the base of the tank. However, if the base and the walls of the tank are monolithic, the wall cannot deform at the base to develop this tensile force because of the restraint produced by the junction of the wall and the base. At the base, the only action produced on the wall is a vertical bending moment due to the corner restraint. Fig. 12.4a shows the linear variation of the hydrostatic pressure from zero at the top to a maximum of p max $= \gamma H$ at the base where it is the depth of liquid in the tank. If there were no restraint at the base, i.e. if the wall was free to expand and slide over the base, then the tensile force would vary linearly also. However, the wall and base are usually monolithic and the deflected shape of the wall is given in Fig. 12.4b. Due to this restraint, the variation of the tensile force is altered and a typical variation is given in Fig. 12.4c. The maximum value of T will be

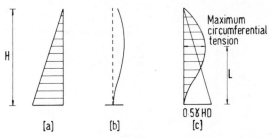

12.4   (a) Horizontal pressure on wall of circular tank. (b) Deflected form of wall of circular tank. (c) Internal forces in wall of circular tank.

considerably less than the value if there was no restraint and will occur at a height L above the base of the tank. Tables of cofficients to determine the values of the maximum circumferential tensile force and its position and the value of the vertical bending moment produced in the wall at the base are given in many textbooks, for example Table 97 in Reynolds and Steedman[4].

Analyses of rectangular tanks   If the horizontal dimensions of the tank are large, then the walls tend to act as vertical cantilevers, except that near the corners, a horizontal bending moment is produced by the restraint of the corner.

In small tanks, the dimensions are such that the problem is a little more complex. When the ratio of the length of a wall to the height is less than about 3, the wall becomes a rectangular two way spanning slab supported on 3 or 4 sides and under the action of a triangularly distributed load as shown in Fig. 12.5. This is a standard problem and tables of coefficients for the bending moments produced in the wall for various ratios of height to length are given in many textbooks, for example Table 40[4].

Analyses of tank floors   The floor of the tank must be designed to resist the moments which are produced when the tank is empty and the surrounding water table is high. This is again the problem of a two way spanning slab under the action of a uniform load and supported on all four sides in the case of a rectangular tank or all round the circumference in the case of a circular tank. Tabulated coefficients for this case are available in most textbooks.

12.2.3   Design of water retaining structures

General   Because of the importance of the serviceability states in the design of water retaining structures, the main criteria for design are based on limiting the amount of cracking which will occur in the concrete at normal working loads. At present, this is accomplished in the relevant code of practice[3] by designing in two ways. The first is based on the normal working stress method in which the concrete is assumed to carry no tensile stress and the section is designed so that the permissible stresses given in the code of practice for the

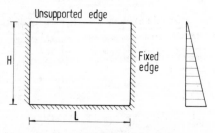

12.5   Wall of rectangular tank.

reinforcing steel and concrete are not exceeded. The second design criterion considers the resistance of the concrete to cracking and should be considered for any tension face in contact with the liquid or for any remote tension face where the member is less than 225 mm thick. The concrete is assumed to be capable of carrying a small tensile stress. The whole cross-section is assumed to be uncracked and is used to calculate the tensile stress on the concrete under the action of a direct tensile force or a bending moment. This tensile stress must not exceed the permissible values given for various strengths of concrete given in the code of practice.

Two main design problems occur in this type of structure: firstly, that the section is under the action of a direct force, tension or compression; and secondly, that the section is under the action of a bending moment. The treatment of these two cases is different and will be illustrated in the next two sections. In certain circumstances, it is possible that a combination of a direct force and a bending moment could occur. If this happens, it is advisable to consult one of the many textbooks on the design of reinforced concrete structures. Because of the high strength of concrete in compression, the case of a direct compressive force is seldom a problem in these structures, since the whole section remains uncracked and capable of resisting the force.

Design of sections for strength   In the case of a section under the action of a tensile force, which would normally be in the walls of a circular tank, the maximum value of the tensile force and the position at which it acts on the wall are found. The concrete is assumed to be incapable of carrying any tensile stress so the whole tensile force must be resisted by the circumferential reinforcing steel. The area of steel required to resist the tensile force is given by the expression

$$Ast = \frac{T}{pst} \ldots \tag{12.1}$$

where
  Ast is the area of reinforcing steel per unit length of wall
  T is the tensile force per unit length of wall
  pst is the permissible steel stress in tension as defined by the code of practice.

If a section has to resist a bending moment, it is normal to neglect any compression steel and to design on the basis of considering only steel in the tension face of the section. Consider a unit length of the section as shown in Fig. 12.6. If this section has to resist a bending moment, then the effective depth of the section, as defined in Fig. 12.6, can be found from the equation

$$M = \tfrac{1}{2}pcbn^1 \left(1 - \frac{n^1}{3}\right) d_1{}^2 \ldots \tag{12.2}$$

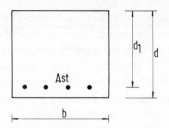

12.6   Unit length of reinforced concrete slab.

where

$$n^1 = \frac{mpcb}{mpcb - pst}$$

and where

M is the applied bending moment per unit length of wall
d_1 is the effective depth of the section
m is the modular ratio of steel and concrete
pcb is the permissible bending compression stress in the concrete
pst is the permissible bending tension stress in the reinforcing steel.

Once the effective depth of the section has been found, the area of reinforcing steel per unit length of section can be found from

$$Ast = \tfrac{1}{2} \frac{pcb}{pst} n^1 d_1 \ldots \tag{12.3}$$

If it is decided that the effective depth as found by equation 12.2 is too small for some reason, the effective depth can be increased to any convenient amount. The steel area required will correspondingly be reduced and the new steel area can be found from the expression

$$M = Ast\, pst \left(1 - \frac{n^1}{3}\right) d_1 \ldots \tag{12.4}$$

Once the effective depth of the section is known, the overall depth can be found by allowing an additional depth of concrete to cover the reinforcing steel.

Design of sections for resistance to cracking   In the design of a section for resistance to cracking, the complete section is considered to be uncracked and the properties calculated on the basis of the equivalent concrete area.

If the section shown in Fig. 12.6 is under the action of a tensile force, then the resulting tensile stress is taken to be

$$f_t = \frac{T}{(m - 1)Ast + d} \ldots \tag{12.5}$$

where d is the overall depth of the section.

If the same section is under the action of a bending moment, then the corresponding tensile stress is found from

$$f_t = \frac{My_1}{I} \dots$$ (12.6)

where I is the second moment of area of the equivalent concrete section about the neutral axis and y_1 is the distance from the neutral axis to the tensile area.

If the tensile stresses found from equations (12.5) and (12.6) exceed the permissible values given in the code of practice, the thickness of the concrete or the area of reinforcing steel must be increased to reduce the stress to the permissible value.

Design of small tanks   It is quite possible, in the case of small tanks, that the minimum thickness of the sections will be determined by constructional restraints rather than by the maximum applied bending moments and direct forces. There is a minimum thickness of concrete wall which can be constructed adequately, bearing in mind the necessity for the high quality workmanship required to get a satisfactory concrete. This minimum thickness will be a function of the height of the walls, but it would be difficult to ensure complete compaction of the concrete if the overall wall thickness is less than 125–150 mm.

However, this does not mean that it is unnecessary to attempt some form of analysis. Unless the maximum forces and moments are calculated, it is not possible to determine whether or not any given thickness is adequate.

Additional requirements   As in any code of practice, certain minimum requirements are specified regarding various points of design, and the code must be consulted on these. For example, if for some reason the thickness of a wall is chosen to be greater than necessary, the area of steel required to resist the applied moments and forces can become smaller. It is possible that if the steel provided at any section is too low, there is a high risk of the concrete cracking due to shrinkage and thermal movements of the concrete. To prevent this, the code of practice specifies a minimum area of steel which must be provided at any section, even though it is not required to resist the forces. An area of steel equal to 0.3% of the gross cross-sectional area of the concrete must be provided in each of two perpendicular directions.

12.3   Construction

12.3.1   General
In any concrete structure, the success, or failure, of the structure depends to a large extent on the care taken in the construction. In view of the stringent environmental restrictions on sewage works, and the importance played by the quality of the concrete on properties such as permeability and durability, it is

even more essential that great stress should be laid on the careful construction of these structures.

Very often, sewage plants of the type dealt with in this work will be located in remote places and it is likely that the concrete will be mixed on site. It is essential that adequate supervision is provided to ensure that the concrete is mixed in the correct proportions so that a uniform water-tight concrete is obtained with the required workability and strength.

Particular attention must also be paid to the placing of the concrete so that a properly compacted and impermeable concrete is obtained. The concrete should be vibrated throughout the construction to prevent the occurrence of honey-combing of the concrete, but it should be realized that too much vibration can result in segregation of the concrete particles with the subsequent increase in permeability and decrease in strength. Segregation can also occur if the concrete is dropped any height into the wall shuttering through a cage of reinforcing steel. Unless special precautions are taken, such as the use of trunking or tremies, concrete should not drop more than 1–1.2 metres through a cage of reinforcement.

12.3.2   Joints

There are two distinct types of joints in concrete structures. Temporary joints – construction joints – are used to facilitate the construction of the structure and if they are properly made, should have no effect on the strength of the structure. Permanent joints – movement joints – are provided in the structure to control the effect of shrinkage, thermal movements and deformations of the structure during its working life. In certain circumstances, these movement joints can effect the behaviour of the structure. If, for example, the reinforcement is stopped at a joint, this joint constitutes a zone of weakness and this should be taken into account in the analysis in that no bending moment and perhaps no shear forces, can be transmitted across the joint.

Whether or not a construction joint is required, will depend on the size of the tank and the method of mixing and placing the concrete. A common spacing of these joints would be about 3–4 metres vertically and 6 metres horizontally. If it is necessary to have a construction joint, great care should be taken in cleaning the face of the joint to ensure a good mechanical connection between the two concretes. The provision of a key between the two pourings will improve the performance of the joint.

Variations in the ambient temperature and shrinkage due to drying out of the concrete can give rise to high strains in the concrete, and if an effort is not made to control these movements, damage to the structure can result, perhaps in the form of indiscriminate cracking of the concrete and subsequent leakage. The provision of properly detailed movement joints, either of an expansive or contracting nature, will solve this problem. If the joint is vertical, a P.V.C. water bar can be used, but if the joint is horizontal, then it is better to use a flat steel plate for the water bar to make sure that the concrete is compacted properly.

12.4 Resistance to Corrosion

Concrete which has been made with the correct type of cement and which has been properly proportioned, mixed and placed will be resistant to most chemical attack, particularly in a purely domestic sewage works, so that in general no special precautions need be taken to protect the concrete. However, any exposed metal, such as plant and machinery, should be given some form of protective coating such as a coat of coal tar base paint to inhibit corrosion.

One problem which demands particular attention is the risk of the concrete being attacked by an external source. In particular, if the groundwater around the plant has a high concentration of sulphate salts, serious damage can occur in the concrete if it is made from ordinary Portland cement. If such a situation is suspected, and this can be verified by a chemical analysis of the groundwater and soil, then it may be necessary to use a special sulphate resisting cement for the concrete.

References

[1] British Standard Code of Practice CP 110: 1972, *The Structural Use of Concrete*, British Standards Institution, London, 1972.
[2] British Standard Code of Practice CP 2005: 1968, *Sewerage*, British Standards Institution, London, 1968.
[3] British Standard Code of Practice CP 2007: 1960, *Design and Construction of Reinforced and Prestressed Concrete Structures for the storage of water and other aqueous liquids*.
[4] *Reinforced Concrete Designers' Handbook*, C. E. Reynolds and J. C. Steedman, Viewpoint Publications, London, 8th Ed., 1974.

13 Pumps and pumping of sewage

13.1 Introduction

Pumping of sewage is to be avoided, if possible, since it usually forms the weakest link in the operation of a system. This does not mean that a pump must be a source of difficulties in the operation of a sewage plant, but it must be chosen and sited with full knowledge of its capabilities. A pump is a machine which generates a flow of a fluid through a system, and in this process produces enough energy to overcome the resistance of this system. The pump is never pre-set to produce a pressure, but will automatically displace the volume of fluid against a system resistance depending on the pump type and its characteristics, which have to match those of the system in which it will operate.

13.2 Pumping of sewage and system resistance

The basic problems associated with the pumping of sewage are twofold.

The first problem stems from the physical properties of the liquid which usually carries solids with a tendency to settle in the piping. To avoid this contingency, it is usual to maintain flow velocities of 0.75 m/s down to 0.6 m/s in rising mains of 100 mm down to 75 mm diameter, depending on the type of sludge. The larger diameter and higher velocity are essential where raw sludge is to be pumped. In general it is desirable to keep the flow velocities in pipes within the range of 1.5 to 2.5 m/s to avoid the rapid increase in resistance to flow which occurs below a velocity of 1.2 m/s. Above this value, the resistance varies primarily with the concentration of the sludge. This is illustrated in Fig. 13.1, which shows a marked increase in the pipe friction factor as compared with values for clean water. In general, a value of a multiplying factor of 2.0 to 2.5 is a reasonable approximation, assuming a moisture content of about 96%.

The second problem arises due to the fact that sludge may lie for considerable periods, sometimes longer than one year. The anaerobic conditions, which would prevail, may produce corrosive gases which can shorten the pump life considerably.

13.2.1 Estimation of system resistance

The resistance of any fluid flow system will consist of three basic components. (see Fig. 13.2) These basic components of system resistance are listed below.

116

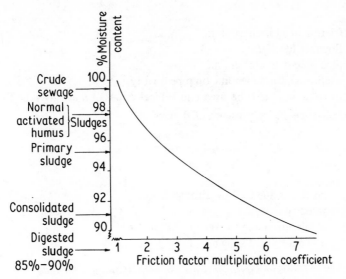

13.1   Friction factor multiplication constant as function of water content.

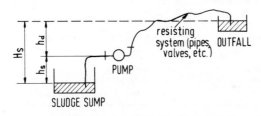

13.2   Diagrammatic system layout.

1.   The Static Lift (H_s) which is the total vertical height through which the liquid has to be raised and which is subdivided into:

(a) suction lift (h_s) which is the vertical height between the liquid level in the sump or sludge vessel and suction inlet of the pump;

(b) delivery lift (h_d) which is the vertical height from the suction inlet of the pump to the discharge level of the delivery pipe.

Thus: $$H_s = h_s + h_d \ldots \tag{13.1}$$

2.   Frictional resistance of piping and fittings. This can be evaluated as follows:

(a) piping resistance is estimated from a suitable friction formula applicable to the piping used in the installation. This formula can take the form

$$h = 7952 \times 10^9 \times \left(\frac{Q \times n}{d^{8/3}}\right)^2 \text{ for clean water} \ldots \tag{13.2}$$

where
   h − friction head in m/1000 m
   q − flowrate in m^3/h
   d − pipe bore diameter in mm
   n − friction factor depending on pipe quality.
Other formulae may also be used and typical values of n are given in Table 13.1

   (b)   resistance due to presence of fittings

$$h_{ftg} = \frac{C \times V^2}{2g} \dots \tag{13.3}$$

where
   h_{ftg} − head loss due to flow through fitting
   V − velocity in m/s
   g − acceleration due to gravity (9.8 m/s^2)
   C − loss coefficient shown in Table 13.2

Table 13.1   *Friction coefficients for use with Manning's formula*

Pipe material	Condition	Value of n
Coated iron and steel pipes	New	0.010
Uncoated iron pipes	New	0.011
Galvanised iron pipes	New	0.012
Vitrified clay pipes	After some weeks of service	0.012
Iron and steel pipes	After use	0.013
All pipes	With imperfect joints and in bad condition	0.015

Courtesy of R. E. Bartlett[1] and Applied Science Publishers.

3.   Leaving loss at the outfall terminal

$$h_{1t} = \frac{V^2}{2g} \dots \tag{13.4}$$

where
   V − velocity of flow
   g − acceleration due to gravity (9.8 m/s^2).
If we assume a velocity of 2.5 m/s in a pipe work which incorporates typical components such as Reflux Valve, Bellmouth, Sluice Valve and 3 bends, the losses under the headings 2(b) and (3) will amount to

$$\Sigma h = \frac{6.25}{2g} (1 + 0.1 + 0.15 + 0.75 + 1)$$

$$= \frac{18.75}{19.82} = 0.945 \text{ m} \dots \tag{13.5}$$

Table 13.2   *Velocity head in fittings and valves*

Fitting	Coefficient (C)
Belmouth	0.10
Bend	0.25 to 0.50
Tee-junction	1.00
Sluice valve	0.15
Reflux valve (single flap)	0.70 to 2.00*

* The value of C for reflux valves increases as the velocity decreases.

Courtesy of R. E. Bartlett[1] and Applied Science Publishers.

It is thus patently obvious that the main losses are due to the static lift and pipe friction losses specified under items 1 and 2(a) respectively. A typical variation of system resistance with flowrate is shown in Fig. 13.3. From Fig. 13.3 it can be seen that:

Total system resistance $= H +$ friction losses + leaving loss
$$= h_s + h_d + \text{pipe losses} + \text{fitting losses} + \text{leaving loss} \ldots$$

$$(13.6)$$

In the above equation h_s varies with the sump level and the fitting losses and leaving losses are usually small. It can be seen from Fig. 13.3 that, as the level in the sump changes, the pump must not only supply more energy to remove the fluid from the sump to the discharge level, but has also to produce an increasing suction lift in order to draw liquid up from the sump into the pump suction inlet branch. This is a most important aspect of pumping and has decisive influence on the selection of a pump suitable for installation. If possible, the pump should always be located below the minimum level of the sump to ensure unassisted priming. This is accomplished by using a submersible unit or placing the pump in a dry well.

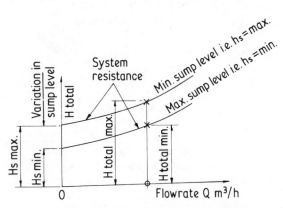

13.3   Typical system resistance variation.

13.3   Types of Pumps

13.3.1   Positive displacement pumps

These will employ a plunger, diaphragm or some type of rotor as exemplified by the Mono Pump, for displacing the fluid. Their salient features are:

They are self priming – usually suction lifts of up to 3–4 m, and as a consequence they may be located above ground and are readily available for inspection.

The flowrate is largely independent of resistance to flow and varies directly with speed of rotation within a specified range.

There is no limit to the pressure which they may overcome, except the mechanical strength of components and the power available for driving. For this reason safety links or pins are provided and these can be quickly and cheaply replaced.

The plunger and diaphragm pumps are fitted with large, easily accessible non return valves.

The rotor types must incorporate some screening and macerating device at suction. Such a device usually forms part of the rotor.

Typical characteristics are shown in Fig. 13.4. It is obvious that such pumps may be particularly suitable for installations requiring small flows and offering a high flow resistance. The term 'force pump' is sometimes used to describe this type of machine, especially when it is of piston or diaphragm type.

13.3.2   Rotodynamic pumps

Pumps of this type employ a rotating element in a stationary casing with a variety of drive layouts. The rotating element, which induces flow, has no direct control over the flowrate and this results in a unit which has a non-overloading characteristic as opposed to the positive displacement pumps where a blockage

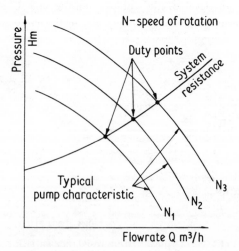

13.4   Positive displacement pump characteristic and system resistance matching.

in the discharge line may result in overloading of the prime mover or mechanical damage. The impeller is shaped to facilitate the passage of solids and can incorporate a device for disintegrating stringy materials, but this is not always necessary. Recent developments in sealing of rotating shafts have made it possible to produce these machines in a form where the combined pump and motor unit operate submerged in the sump. They can readily be lifted out for maintenance due to the invention of automatic pipe coupling devices. A typical pump of this type is shown in Fig. 13.5, and its flow and head characteristics are shown in Fig. 13.6.

13.4 Pump operation and matching

The operation of a pump can be either manual or automatic, and the most usual automatic actuation method is by float switches operating at the upper and lower sump level positions.

The most common type of operation for a small sewage plant would employ a submersible, electrically driven unit with float operated switches or a programmed time switching sequence. For very small installations, a positive displacement rotor pump incorporating a macerating device can be very successful. The matching of the pump characteristics and system resistance can be accomplished by superimposing the system resistance range over the pump characteristic on the total head/flow rate diagram. This will show whether the pump will maintain a reasonable efficiency over the range of operating conditions.

In the case of a positive displacement pump, the speed of rotation must be adequate to produce the flow and the power within the strength of components.

In the case of a rotodynamic pump, the maximum system resistance has to intercept the pump characteristic at a flow which will be in excess of that which will produce settling of solids (i.e. in excess of 1.3 m/s in the pipe). The principal details which have to be ascertained before choosing a pump, or when specifying requirements to a pump maker are listed below.

A. Type of prime mover
B. Flowrate
C. Total Resistance head
    1. Static lift
    2. Suction lift
    3. Pipe dimensions ⎤
                    ⎬ or specify friction losses
    4. Fittings ⎦
D. Type of sewage
E. Type of pump
    1. Fixed or portable
    2. Self priming
    3. Submersible
    4. Dry well (flooded suction)
F. Operating control method

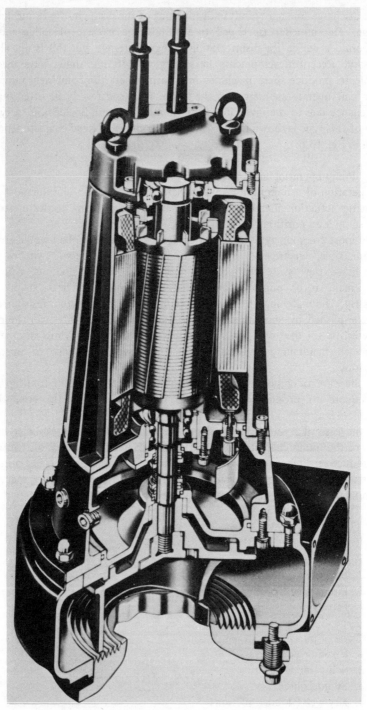

13.5   Typical submersible centrifugal pump (Courtesy of Mono-Pumps).

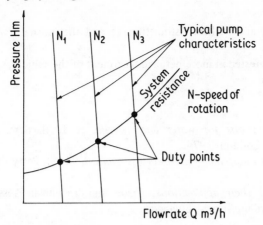

13.6   Centrifugal pump characteristics and system resistance matching.

In general, it is advisable to supply the pump maker with drawings of the installation site and to seek his approval and advice before deciding on a final method of installation.

13.5   Maintenance and general usage

In most cases, the pumps require annual inspection with very little, if any, additional maintenance. The piston pump valves may require cleaning out, but these are readily accessible and do not present any problems. The rotodynamic pumps are by and large trouble free unless there is a seal failure which can lead to serious consequences in a submersible unit.

In the unlikely event of such a failure, the pump may have to be replaced completely, but this is not a major undertaking, since it is readily withdrawn and a standard replacement unit may be substituted. It is not a skilled operation, except for completion of electrical connections.

Portable submersible sewage pumps with hydraulic motor drive taken off a tractor powered source are also becoming available at the present time, and can be used where only occasional pumping is necessary. The variety of pumps available on the market is so great that it is virtually impossible to make any specific recommendations; however, as a general rule, it may be stated that the general duties for various pump types are approximately as follows:

Type of pump	*Flow rate*	*Pressures head*
Positive displacement	Up to $1 m^3/h$	Limitation due to strength of pump only
Rotodynamic (unchokable)	In excess of $1 m^3/h$	Up to 20 m

It must be stressed that this is only a rough guide, and expert advice should be sought before making any decisions. The two suitable sources of enquiries could be the British Pump Makers Association[2] and the journal, *Pumps and their applications*[3].

For those interested in more detailed treatment of the subject, some reading in depth is essential.

References

[1] *Pumping stations for water and sewage*, R. E. Bartlett, Appl. Science Publishers, London, 1974.
[2] *The British Pump Manufacturers Association*, 94–98 Petty France, London SW1.
[3] *Pumps and their applications*, Trade and Technical Press Ltd., Crown House, Morden, Surrey, England.

14 Operation and maintenance of small sewage works

The maintenance required at any sewage works depends upon the size of the site, the treatment process and the nature of the sewage treated. Large sewage works have professionally qualified residential managers and supporting laboratory facilities. Single houses with any form of sewage treatment will have no qualified supervision. All of the treatment processes require some attention and, to maintain effective treatment, it is essential that regular maintenance is carried out. While there are well documented procedures available, particularly for percolating filters[1], other methods — e.g. rotating biological filters and package activated sludge plants — have less accessible documentation of operation and maintenance procedures. The following outline of operation and maintenance requirements is intended to serve as an introductory summary. Exact details — situation of valves, electrical connections, lubrication — are not included as they vary between each plant, and details can often be obtained from the equipment manufacturers. Certain of the points have been made in other sections but are collated in this chapter. The implementation of the routines in individual plants is a matter of experience. It is, however, important to understand the reasons for particular operations so that work schedules can be arranged to suit local circumstances.

The discussion has been arranged in the approximate sequential order of biological sewage treatment, preliminary treatment, settlement, biological processes, sludge disposal, tertiary treatment and mechanical equipment. The major processes of sewage treatment, septic tanks, activated sludge, percolating filters and rotating biological filters are discussed. Other methods which are usually modifications of these basic processes are not included — operators often have to rely upon the information supplied by manufacturers, particularly for less popular treatment methods.

14.1 Septic tanks

Septic tanks require little supervision; they rely upon settlement of solids and some anaerobic digestion. If correctly designed, the former more important process operates satisfactorily. The process does not require an electrical supply,

125

only generates a small head loss and can easily be sited. The major operation required is periodic desludging. The normal period between desludging is 6–12 months; the precise period depends upon the size of the tank relative to the nature and volume of the sewage flow. The tanks should be desludged when they are approximately half full of sludge, removing five sixths of the actual sludge and leaving one sixth as an anaerobic seed material; see Chapter 6. Septic tank sludges are malodorous and the desludging process should be completed as efficiently as possible. It is usually necessary to arrange for a tanker service to desludge the septic tank. Ready reliable access to the site must be available. It is often convenient to desludge the tank before the winter. This usually ensures adequate access and extra capacity in the empty tank prior to the period when the least anaerobic digestion will occur. During the desludging (or commissioning) of a two compartment tank, it is advisable to ensure that equal pressures are exerted on each side of the dividing compartment.

It is preferable to carry out inspections of the tank at regular intervals (weekly, monthly), to check the volume of sludge and ensure that flow through the tank is satisfactory. The most common blockage point is at the inlet, disposable nappies being common blocking agents. The common complaints against septic tanks – odours and poor effluents – are partly inherent in the processes. High flows are liable to disturb and wash out the settled sludges, giving high suspended solids values in the effluent. The formation of a scum on the liquid surface can partly reduce odours; the breakdown of the scum under high flows or after desludging may be responsible in part for odours.

In general, septic tanks are cheap, require little attention beyond inspection and desludging and, if properly designed, can be capable of producing effluents below 100 mg/l suspended solids.

14.2 Preliminary treatment

14.2.1 Screens

The common form of preliminary treatment at a small works is a hand raked screen. The screen traps any large materials in the sewage, e.g. rags, plastic, but in doing so becomes blocked. Once partially blocked, the screen traps smaller but often more offensive objects, e.g. faeces. The screens require regular raking and washing with water or sewage. The screenings require disposal; often this is by burial. It is usually necessary to rake the screens at least once per day. Activated sludge plants which site the screen prior to the final settlement tank should require less attention than those at the inlet. More regular raking is needed if a high proportion of large solids is anticipated. This occurs during storms for sewage works which include surface water drainage. Particularly the first flush of storm water after a period of dry weather is likely to include a high concentration of large solids and consequently to block the screens. At times of storm water flows, more regular clearance of the screens is therefore required. In winter, at exposed sites, the screens can begin to ice up and again can restrict sewage flow. The erection of a wind break near the screen is often sufficient to prevent icing.

14.2.2 Grit channels

At larger works or those serving areas which drain roads or paths, a grit channel can be included to remove the largest dense settleable particles, grit, sand, which would otherwise interfere or block later processes – pumping, aeration, tank operation. The channels are usually built in pairs and it is necessary to divert the sewage flow and run off any supernatant liquid. The exposed grit can be moved by any convenient means, usually by hand with a shovel. The channel should then be washed clean and any mechanical equipment inspected and lubricated. The removed grit can be dried and dumped or used as a fill material.

The regularity of this process depends upon the accumulation of grit in the channel at a particular works. Weekly grit removal is often convenient, again with additional removal particularly after storms.

14.2.3 Storm tanks

Particularly in larger works and for sewages which include surface water, flows greater than the design flow (often 3 times dry weather flow) are diverted to holding tanks. Although not strictly preliminary treatment, it is convenient to discuss the operation and maintenance of these tanks at this point. If possible, the supernatant liquid should be returned to the inlet of the works and the sludge removed as described for settlement tanks (14.3). This should be carried out as soon as is convenient to avoid the settled sewage and sludge from turning anaerobic, and to clear the tanks. Again, it is advisable to check and clear the weirs and to carry out regular maintenance of any mechanical equipment.

14.3 Settlement tanks

Two types of settlement tank are common, horizontal and upward flow tanks. These tanks are used for settling raw sewage and more commonly at small activated sludge plants for settling the materials after biological treatment. The design of these tanks was dealt with in Chapter 7. For all settlement tanks it is usually necessary to carry out at least a daily inspection and, as necessary, to clean weirs and remove scum and floating materials.

At small sites the tanks will require desludging by hand, although some of the more recent package plants have included pumps to facilitate the easy removal of sludge. In all cases the aim is to remove all of the accumulated sludge and to include a minimum of water with this sludge.

Horizontal flow tanks require the diversion of the sewage flow, removal of supernatant water and desludging. The empty tank can be cleaned, particularly round the weirs and baffles, mechanical equipment checked, the sludge pipe flushed and sewage flow restarted. It is usually necessary to divert or stop the sewage flow, because there is unlikely to be much spare capacity. The sludges become malodorous if exposed for too long, so these operations should be carried out as quickly as is compatible with effectiveness. Desludging should be completed at least within a day, such that the sludge is not exposed overnight. Horizontal flow tanks require desludging at approximately weekly intervals, depending upon local conditions.

Upward flow tanks can normally be desludged without diverting the flow. Release of a valve from the bottom of the tank permits the outflow of the settled sludge. This should be carried out slowly or in stages to permit the resettlement of the partly disturbed sludge and prevent the withdrawal of commitments to a minimum — usually periodic checking and cleaning of equipment. It is important to estimate the optimum frequency of desludging. If the are more watery than from a horizontal flow tank and sludge drying is therefore more lengthy. Continuous mechanical desludging equipment reduces labour commitments to a minimum — usually periodic checking and cleaning of equipment. It is important to estimate the optimum frequency of desludging. If the desludging is too infrequent the tank may accumulate too much sludge and some of the settleable solids will pass out over the weirs. The sludges can turn anaerobic and the rising gas bubbles will again increase the solids contents of the effluent. In an upward flow tank the accumulation of compacted sludge can block the sludge draw off pipe. This can necessitate the difficult and lengthy process of completely draining the tank. Too frequent desludging will produce a more watery sludge from an upward flow tank and also involve unnecessary labour for a horizontal tank.

Settlement tanks require adequate desludging and daily cleaning of weirs combined with intelligent care of the tanks. The latter point means that the flow over the cleaned outlet weirs should be regular at normal flows. If the tanks shift such that the flow is over only part of the outlet weir it is necessary to make adjustments to more closely approach the design weir loading. Similarly, it is important particularly with upflow tanks to prevent foreign objects from entering the tank (e.g. tools, stones) and interfering with the flow and settlement patterns.

14.4 Biological treatment

14.4.1 Activated sludge
The separate aeration tank of an activated sludge system should require little maintenance. It is again necessary to clean the weirs baffles and scum boards regularly — and these items usually require daily attention. Aeration equipment will require attention at longer time intervals and maintenance information is available from reputable suppliers. For units which use coarse bubble aeration the aerators should not block and an occasional brushing to remove any scum, slime or solids is usually sufficient. Fine bubble diffusers tend to block after continued use and require cleaning. For this it is necessary to divert the flows and either to remove and replace the diffuser domes or to clean the domes *in situ*. The air filters on the blower intakes will require periodic cleaning. Surface

aerators usually only require mechanical maintenance, lubrication, adjustment and replacement. The other tests which are to be carried out involve assessing the sludge volume and sludge quality see Sections 2.4 and 14.5.

14.4.2 Percolating filters

The effective performance of a percolating filter relies upon the growth of the biological film and the even distribution of settled sewage over this film. It is therefore important not only that the filter bed itself is in good condition but that the equipment responsible for dosing the sewage onto the filter is in good condition and of the correct size. Attention therefore has to be paid to the filter bed, the distributors and the dosing equipment.

Dosing equipment In order to achieve the maximum efficiency from a percolating filter it is necessary to ensure that the sewage is evenly distributed over the surface of the filter medium. This is achieved by a dosing system which works by only passing the settled sewage from a holding chamber to the filter when the chamber is nearly full. The force of this liquid will drive the distributor round the filter so electrical power is not necessary at the site. The system is gravity fed; however, there is a significant head loss through the entire treatment process (2–3 m).

The settled sewage is therefore fed into a dosing chamber and then via a dosing siphon to the distributor. The dosing chamber requires regular (weekly) cleaning to prevent the accumulation of debris, scum and fat which can interfere with the operation of the siphon. The siphon and air pipes should be kept free of grease and solid matter. Maintenance, particularly of the pipes, should be carried out in accordance with manufacturers exact instructions. The operation of the siphon requires air-tight joints within the piping systems. Normally therefore visual checks and superficial cleaning of the siphon and air pipes are all that can be carried out regularly. Dismantling of the equipment should only be carried out at longer intervals of time (6–12 months) and then with care, in accordance with the suppliers' instructions.

Distributors The sparge holes on the distributor arms require frequent cleaning to ensure an even distribution of settled sewage. This may be necessary on a daily basis or if a fine screen is incorporated in the dosing system less regular cleaning is required. It is sometimes easiest to remove the arms for small filters which avoids the possibility of any larger solids trapped in the arms falling onto the filter surface. Removal of the arms also encourages regular lubrication of the distributor rotation mechanism. The latter requires regular lubrication usually as recommended by the suppliers. The distributor is driven by the flow of settled sewage and therefore smooth easy motion is essential. The height of the distributor arms should be adjusted, usually with guy ropes, to make sure that each arm receives an equal flow. Stationary distributors require similar attention, also cleaning and checking of levels and tipping troughs.

Sewage in the siphons and distributors has a tendency to freeze, particularly during winter nights when low temperatures are combined with low flows. The dosing equipment can be covered with tarpaulins to afford some protection. Recirculation is a useful method of preventing freezing if this is possible. When out of use both siphons and distributors should be completely drained to reduce both corrosion and ice formation.

Filter bed The filter bed itself should require little real attention and excessive walking on the bed should be avoided as it tends to crush the stones and reduce void spaces in the bed. If it is necessary to walk on the bed planks should be laid to spread the load. The surface of the bed should be kept clear of weeds and moss, any ponded area which may form in the winter months should be lightly forked over or treated with a suitable chemical as directed (sodium nitrate). The filter bed should have a plentiful supply of air to maintain the general aerobic conditions. This air is supplied through ventilation shafts, pipes and channels, and such ventilation should be regularly checked and any obstruction removed.

14.4.3 Rotating biological filters

Rotating biological filters are usually purchased as a package plant and as such incorporate primary settlement facilities, the disc units and final settlement. The settlement areas require similar general maintenance to other settlement or septic tanks – general cleaning of weirs etc., and desludging. The rotating disc unit itself requires little attention. The main bearing usually requires periodic lubrication in accordance with the manufacturers instruction. A daily check should be made to be certain that the filter is rotating. The most difficult problems are created by a breakdown of the disc rotation due to a mechanical or electrical failure. The provision of an audio/visual warning of rotation failure is advantageous. Although rotation of a fully balanced disc requires little power, the starting of rotation creates a significant torque on the shaft system. If the rotation has stopped for a long period, the exposed biomass will become dehydrated and die. This produces an unbalanced disc which creates an erratic load on the drive system. It is therefore important to minimise the periods of rotation failure, and, if an extensive stoppage occurs, the discs can usually be rotated by hand to prevent eccentric loading.

14.5 Activated sludge package plants

Activated sludge package plants should be designed on similar principles to conventional activated sludge plants. The plants with separate settlement and aeration facilities require maintenance as detailed in the individual unit operations. The smaller plants do not usually have separate primary settlement. The aeration and final settlement tank, weirs, baffles and scum boards require daily cleaning and any surface fat or grease which is often present as relatively large fat balls should be removed and disposed of separately. The aeration equipment should be visually checked to ascertain that adequate aeration and mixing is present. A 30 minute settlement test of the mixed liquor should be carried out to check the settlement characteristics of the activated sludge. The level of sludge in the final settlement tank should be checked and when necessary the tank desludged. The necessity of desludging depends upon the concentration of solids and the settlement characteristics of the sludge. While some tanks need desludging when half full others can tolerate 80% of sludge without adverse effects upon the effluent, individual cases should be decided in the light of local experience.

Activated sludge plants require some return of sludge. In the smallest plants this can be non positive while the larger plants all have positive sludge return via electric or air lift pumps. The working of these pumps should be checked daily and any blockage e.g. by paper or leaves should be freed.

Rapid opening and closing of the valves which control the supply of air to airlifts causes surges in the air lifts and minimises clogging. It us usually advisable to carry out this process at regular intervals (weekly, monthly). Minor adjustments of the pump rates should also be made to optimise efficiency by preventing the accumulation of solids in the settlement tank, or too high an M.L.S.S. in the aeration tank.

14.6 Sludge beds

If sludge is not removed by a tanker service, the usual process at a small works is to dry the sludge on drying beds. The beds should be exposed to any prevailing winds and all unnecessary wind breaks should be avoided. Evaporation is the major drying mechanism in sludge beds, so exposure to wind is advantageous. Experience suggests that about 22 cm (9 in) of sludge dries quickest. If feasible, a few days after running in the sludge any excess water should be removed and recirculated through the sewage works. The sludge should be removed once spadeable and disposed of. The time for drying varies greatly usually depending upon local rainfall, temperature and wind. It is therefore best to inspect the beds regularly and to remove the sludge as soon as is suitable, particularly before the winter when drying is poorest. The original 22 cm of wet sludge should give approximately 7 cm of drier sludge which is usually removed in barrows on a small site.

14.7 Aerobic digestion

Some small plants incorporate facilities for the aerobic digestion of waste sludge. Such facility may be particularly useful at a camping or caravan site when a rapid start up is required. The aerobic digestion tank requires little maintenance. The aeration of the tank is usually stopped each day and supernatant liquid returned to the inlet of the works. Similarly feed to the digestion tank from the settlement tank usually occurs on a daily basis. These operations are often controlled by time clocks to occur at times of low flow. The operation and timing of these pumping operations should be checked regularly. When almost full the aerobic digester requires desludging. The aeration equipment and pumps require the same attention as described previously.

14.8   Mechanical equipment

A range of mechanical and electro/mechanical equipment is present at sewage works, and it all requires regular checking and maintenance. In general manufacturers can supply detailed instructions for the regular maintenance of this equipment and these should be strictly followed. The commonest operation is lubrication e.g. on pump and shaft bearings and distributor arms. The ancillary equipment e.g. floats or electrodes for the control of pumps from sumps should be inspected, cleaned and lubricated as necessary. The simplest daily operation is to check that motors are not overheating.

14.9   Tertiary treatment

14.9.1   Grass plots

The irrigation of effluent from a biological treatment plant over an even grass plot can reduce the load contained in the effluent. The distribution of liquids should be regular such that channels do not form and the bulk of the liquid contacts the soil. A regular check of the distribution of liquid from a nozzle or channel and the level of the plot should be made and any obvious defects corrected. The grass needs cutting to maintain a reasonable but not excessive growth. Clearly in winter little cutting is required while in summer very regular cutting is needed (weekly, or every 2 weeks). The grass cuttings should be removed and disposed of separately.

The grass area is normally divided into several plots and only part of the total area is irrigated at any one time. The flow should be diverted from an active to a fallow plot as required. Again local conditions of soil type and irrigation liquid dictate the times of a given run. Usually once percolation becomes restricted, irregularities in the plot area become significant or large numbers of rank weeds appear the changeover should be made, monthly intervals are often convenient. If a plot receives a particularly high load of suspended solids, these can accumulate on the surface of the plot. In summer this creates less problem as a dry sludge can be raked off with the grass cuttings. In winter parts of the plot can become sodden and in the spring it may be necessary to returf or re-seed parts or all of a plot.

14.9.2   Sand filters

Sand filters effectively remove some of the solid particles in an effluent, although there is some biological action. In removing the solid particles the sand bed becomes clogged and the flow through the bed becomes very slow. When this occurs the flow should be diverted, the bed allowed to dry and the top layer of sand which contains the solids removed and disposed of or washed. A layer of fresh sand is added and the bed can be re-used. The frequency of clogging of the bed again depends upon the suspended solids load on the bed. Weekly cleaning is often convenient. Rapid sand filters are usually cleaned by backwashing.

14.9.3 Pebble bed clarifiers

Pebble bed clarifiers are commonly installed as tertiary treatment processes to package activated sludge plants. Their operation is similar to that of sand beds except that the material collects between larger pores and some flocculation occurs. Due to the larger pores in a pebble bed clarifier hydraulic flow is not seriously impaired even when the bed is heavily loaded. Instead the solid materials begin to break through the bed, becoming visible as a sludge on the surface stones of the upward flow bed and the effluent quality decreases. At this time the bed should be backwashed usually while raking the bed. The resulting wash liquid is passed to the settlement tank. Again it is often convenient to carry out this operation on a weekly basis. Where a clarifier has been purchased from a manufacturer, the detailed instructions should be followed as to exact backwash procedure.

14.10 General works

A brief summary of the operation and maintenance requirements of each of the processes is given in Table 14.1. The table only indicates a general requirement e.g. check may require a visual inspection, cleaning, stripping of equipment and/or lubrication. In all works except septic tanks daily maintenance is required, usually for general cleaning purposes. On a less regular basis desludging is the major operation required for all types of plants. These two basic operations are vital for the effective treatment of sewage, since without them little or no treatment is really given at any works. The maintenance suggestions given by suppliers of equipment should be followed. The data given on mechanical equipment e.g. pumps is usually very sound and can be strictly followed. The data for the treatment processes cannot be as useful and needs to be applied in the light of local conditions and experience.

14.10.1 Attention to site

The psychological advantage of maintaining a clean well kept site cannot be over emphasized. The presence of well kept grounds, clean buildings and well finished structures encourages operators to ensure that the treatment plant itself works well. The works should be kept generally tidy, grass verges round installations should be cut regularly, structures should be painted and maintained. If possible, shrubs and flowers can be planted within the works. Shrubs are additionally useful for camouflaging a sewage works, particularly at sensitive sites. Visitors to an expensive hotel do not necessarily want a bedroom with a view into a sewage works, nor do campers want to be reminded of mundane matters like sewage treatment. Large trees, however, should be avoided as the roots can easily disturb the siting or foundations of a works. Deciduous trees are especially difficult as the leaves falling into the works cause serious

Table 14.1   *Summary of maintenance requirements*

Treatment Process	Required Maintenance		
	Daily	Weekly or Monthly	Annual
Septic Tank		Inspect tank and inlets	Desludge
Screens	Rake and clear		
Settlement Tanks			
Horizontal flow	Clean weirs	Desludge and check	
Upward flow	Clean weirs	Desludge	Drain and check
Percolating Filter	Clean sparge holes	Clean dosing chamber; Check, siphon, pipes distributor, ventilation	Check any mechanical equipment
Activated Sludge Aeration Unit	Clean weirs, baffles, scum board; Measure 30 min settlement; Inspect aeration equipment	Check aerators and sludge pumps	Check aeration equipment
Rotating Disc Package Plant	Clean weirs Check rotation	Desludge Check bearings	Check mechanical equipment
Activated Sludge Package Plant Including Settlement Tank	Clean weirs, baffles, scum boards, remove scum, fat; Measure 30 min settlement; Inspect aeration equipment and sludge return	Desludge settlement tank; Surge air pressures	Check aeration and mechanical equipment
Sludge Beds	Inspect beds	Fill and empty beds	
Aerobic Digester	Settle and repump, Inspect aeration and sludge returns	Desludge	Check aeration equipment
Grass Plots	Check even distribution	Cut and clear grass, Change plots and level	Returf or reseed if necessary
Sand Filters	Inspect	Remove top sand and replace or backwash	Check
Pebble Beds	Inspect	Backwash and rake	Check

problems — blocking air lifts, sparge holes and filter medium. In general, works should be sited away from large and deciduous trees. If such siting is not possible, the effects of roots should be minimized, e.g. by surface siting or only partial burying of works. Wire mesh can be installed over works during the autumn to exclude leaves.

14.10.2   Works safety and security
Sewage can contain a range of pathogenic organisms which are a health hazard. At all sites, therefore, there should be adequate washing facilities for the

plant operatives. As a very minimum there should be a clean water supply. although it is much better if more complete washroom facilities are available. Similarly, other general safety precautions necessary at all sewage works and with electrical equipment should be observed[2]. A first aid box should be provided. Any tank likely to contain noxious or toxic gases e.g. septic tanks, should only be entered under expert supervision. Electrical equipment should only be adjusted with the current disconnected. Electrical equipment can be dangerous if it is wet. Moving mechanical equipment can be dangerous and should be properly screened. While several of these possibilities are only rare occurrences and can only apply at certain sites, an intelligent assessment of all sites is necessary.

All sites are prone to vandalism, and can be potentially dangerous to intruders. A stout fence and lockable gate are obviously needed at all sewage works. At certain sites it is advisable to construct buildings without windows and rely upon artificial light. These precautions tend to discourage vandalism and unauthorised entry.

14.10.3   Routines and records
Besides the operations outlined in the bulk of this chapter, it is obviously of value to sample the liquor at various locations in the works as often as possible. Samples of raw and settled sewage and of final effluent can be collected and visually reported by any operative. The provision of simple sampling equipment, a bucket and rope, a range of clear marked bottles, jars or cylinders to hold the sample for inspection, and a bottle brush to clean the inspection vessel, is very cheap. The changes in appearance of these samples gives a good indication of the performance of individual unit operations and of the plant as a whole, e.g. an increased cloudiness of the effluents may suggest overloading or ineffective aeration or settlement.

It is unlikely that small works will be visited regularly by qualified personnel. It is therefore important that some qualified personnel at least oversee the regular operation and maintenance of plants. This can often be conveniently arranged if the responsible body has several plants under its control. Local authorities with one larger sewage works and several smaller works can sometimes arrange for the manager of the large works to oversee supervision of the smaller works.

In all cases the keeping of useful records of plant operation is invaluable in assessing changes and planning in new works. A diary or log book should be available at the site for relevant comments. One of the most convenient methods is to draw up work schedules for particular operations. These can include daily sheets for the routine cleaning and inspection of the plant and other sheets for a range of other functions – desludging, servicing, sludge drying, tertiary treatment maintenance. An example given (Table 14.2) for a small activated sludge package plant illustrates the type of sheet which can be produced. This ensures that the necessary daily cleaning of the plant taking perhaps an hour is completed and that the plant is operating properly. Additionally the sheets

Table 14.2   *Daily work sheet for small activated sludge package plant*

Strathclyde Sewage Works

Data   /   /

Time

Flow d   . . . . mm^3

Power Consumption   . . . . kWh

Weather . . . .

Appearance of Raw Sewage . . . .

          Mixed Liquor . . . .

          Final Effluent . . . .

Sludge volume after 30 min . . .   . ml

Inspect   Inlet   [   ]

               Outlet   [   ]

               Aerators   [   ]

               Compressor   [   ]

               Air Lifts   [   ]

Rake screens & dispose of screenings [   ]

Clean weirs and baffles   [   ]

Remove scum, grease, fat   [   ]

Comments:

Signed:

document valuable data on the plant – hydraulic loading, power consumption, infiltration, sludge quality, plant performance. This process is also useful in making adequate time available for these operations. Most plants require daily attention of at least 30 mins., but the period involved depends upon the size and complexity of the plant and can be much greater. Additional operations on many plants then require extra time e.g. an hour or more to desludge an upflow settlement tank, time for general site work particularly in the summer, several hours for sludge removal from drying beds.

All reputable manufacturers of mechanical, electrical and sewage treatment units supply instruction manuals to facilitate the operation and servicing of their units. It is clearly advisable that this information be made available to the persons actually involved in the operation of the plant. Too often the instructions are neatly filed away in the office of the person responsible for purchasing the plant. The most effective method is to hold one reference copy filed away, but to make a copy available to the plant operator.

Only generalized conclusions can be drawn about the relative times required to ensure the effective working of the various types of works. Septic tanks are very simple and require little or no regular attention. Rotating biological filters need an electricity supply and require more attention but are still relatively undemanding. Percolating filters have more moving parts than the similar rotating biological filters. The operation of percolating filters is still fairly self regulating, the attention required is general and can be classed as moderate. The activated sludge process is generally considered to require the most expert supervision at large works and experience suggests that similar generalization apply to smaller works. Daily visits are essential for the effective operation of the process and to obtain optimum treatment minor modifications of the plant variables are often required.

14.11 Start-up and close-down of sewage works
All types of sewage works serving any type of community require some period of acclimatisation during which time an adequate population of biological species can be established. Certain treatment processes are capable of a rapid start-up (activated sludge), while others require a more lengthy period of acclimatisation (percolating filter). Treatment plants for small fixed communities are unlikely to be taken out of commission while camping and caravan sites are often closed for six months every year. The processes of start-up and close-down are discussed for activated sludge and biological filter plants.

14.11.1 Activated sludge plants
The time required to start up a small scale plant and begin to produce good quality effluents can vary between a few days and several weeks. Two procedures can be adopted: importing a seed of biological material from another plant or beginning without any separate addition of biological material and allowing the required micro-organisms to build up to the necessary concentration. Provided that the imported activated sludge is not unusual and can adapt

to the new sewage, the plant should be operating effectively in less than a week. It is usually best to begin by aerating the activated sludge mixed with good river water or tap water. After a few hours, raw sewage can be introduced at a low rate, gradually increasing to full load. The use of an aerobic digester to store sludge during the winter at a seasonal site is clearly advantageous. Direct transfer of the aerobically digested sludge avoids the expense and inconvenience of arranging for the import of a seed activated sludge. Although aerobically digested sludge is different in character to normal activated sludge, acclimatisation is again possible within a short period of time. Similarly, the start-up of a duplicate system at time of peak flow should be straightforward by direct transfer of the fully acclimatized activated sludge from the parallel plant.

The natural build-up of biological mass required for all aerobic treatment processes is more lengthy and can involve a period of several weeks. During this period only reduced sewage flows should be passed and effluents are of poor quality, and localised difficulties can occur, e.g. excessive foaming.

Similarly, the shut-down of a plant requires careful attention. After the final flow of sewage, the plant should continue operation for approximately 72 hours to ensure complete treatment of all of the sewage. The aerators should be turned off and the solids allowed to settle for a convenient period of time (12 to 24 hours). The supernatant liquids can usually be discharged into the receiving water – they should be equivalent to final effluent. Sludges can be removed, usually into a sludge tanker. During these processes, an equal pressure should be maintained on either side of any internal partition. Once dry, the tanks, baffles and weirs should be cleaned and all mechanical equipment checked and greased. It is usually convenient to cover the units with a tarpaulin. Clearly, if a high water table exists, care should be taken to avoid flotation during the emptying process and once the plant is empty. If a high water table exists, it will be necessary to refill the units with water during periods of non operation.

14.11.2   Biological filter plants

Many of the points made for activated sludge plants apply equally to biological filter plants. The start-up of biological filter plant is more lengthy. The addition of biological material is not feasible; instead, the procedure must rely upon the slow growth of biomass on the support medium. These systems require several weeks of dosing to 'mature' and provide effective treatment. Best results are obtained if gradually increasing loads can be applied to the works; this permits the steady accumulation of biomass which is required. Similarly, complete closedown is not usually acceptable unless a gradually increasing load can be guaranteed for the following start-up. It is more feasible to continue operation with a very low load. This could be provided either by some small sewage flow or by recycling part of the effluent. Application of a low load will cause dehydration of the growths in a percolating filter. For a rotating biological filter there will be a die back of the biomass such that only the first discs will contain viable micro-organisms. The remaining biomass should provide a useful seed for subsequent increased loads.

If these plants are to be completely closed down, it is advisable to arrange for periods of low loading to reduce the biomass in the aerobic treatment zone and usually to obtain instructions from the commercial suppliers. Precautions to avoid freezing within dosing siphons should be taken together with the general considerations outlined for activated sludge plants.

In general, biological filters, particularly percolating filters, give their best results when required to treat almost constant loads and receive regular dosing with sewage. Rapid start-up is not normally associated with these processes. Careful management of these plants is therefore required to ensure that adequate treatment is possible.

14.12 Additional equipment

At the small and variable communities under consideration actual engineering design is less critical than for larger works. Of much more importance is the accurate prediction of sewage volumes and strengths and the continued management of the plant once in service. No amount of accurate design work will produce a good effluent if a plant is never desludged. Similarly if the design flows are significantly too low then the final effluent will be poor even with good management.

The most useful extra at many plants is therefore overall supervision by some qualified or competent person. Although this may appear obvious the effective management of works makes a great improvement to the appearance and performance of the plant.

Surprizingly few small sewage works, particularly package plants, have flow measurement devices. An accurate knowledge of the flows and flow variations at works permits the good management of a plant and helps to pin-point failures. Two types of simple flow measurement are possible namely V-notch weirs and standing wave flumes. V-notch weirs are simple and can provide measurement of purified liquors such as final effluent; the weirs tend to clog and back up particularly with raw sewage. Standing wave flumes can be installed at any suitable point in a works. The visual, manual spot measurement of flows from a calibrated notch or flume provides some flow information at minimum cost. The installation of an automatic recorder to provide permanent continuous records of the flow patterns is clearly better but is more expensive to install. The value of obtaining flow data, particularly for authorities who expect to instal more than one works, cannot be overstressed. Small works are so prone to hydraulic washout that any device which might help to prevent this is of value.

Besides the daily visual sampling at points in the works it is useful to carry out more detailed analysis. The laboratory analysis for certain critical parameters e.g. B.O.D.$_5$, C.O.D., S.S., nitrate and ammonia can provide valuable information. These data are particularly useful during the first few months of operation but regular samples during subsequent operation provides documented evidence for systematic changes. Particularly for more detailed analysis, spot samples can be misleading and composite samples are often used. This involves collecting several samples over a long period and combining them – e.g. every hour between 7.00

and 19.00. For this purpose an automatic sampling device can be a useful acquisition particularly if required for several sites. Similarly, readily portable instrumentation e.g. pH and D.O. meters can be used for periodic and more detailed checking of a works.

Particular sites can provide problems which necessitate additional equipment. Hotels often produce a sewage high in fat content which accumulates in the sewage works. The provision of a fat or grease trap is therefore important at such a site and such a trap needs regular cleaning. Any sewage which produces large amounts of scum is likely to benefit by installation of a scum pump. Similarly, petrol interceptors may be required at certain specialist sites. Commercial dewatering equipment is expensive and small plants cannot normally afford the cost, but mobile dewatering equipment is now available or, alternatively, tankering wet sludge to a central site for dewatering is feasible.

Ineffective sludge disposal is a major reason for the poor performance of many plants. As an alternative to dumping sludge, agricultural spraying of wet sludge, or further drying and bagging of dewatered sludge for sale as a soil conditioner requires extra equipment but can alleviate an awkward problem. For larger works which have adequate skilled supervision the provision of a heated digester should be considered.

With increasing labour costs the purchase of mechanical equipment is usually justified. The automation of some of the more time consuming jobs e.g. desludging horizontal settlement tanks, can often be worthwhile. Specialist plant manufacturers have equipment for automatically desludging even fairly small tanks.

14.13 Conclusions

The continued maintenance and operation of all plants is critical for the production of a good quality effluent. Attention to the detailed requirements of each works is as important as effective design and construction of the plant. Each type of plant requires different attention and each site imposes a different set of restrictions upon the operation of a plant. The information available from books and manufacturers' literature should be interpreted in the light of local conditions and experience. If managed well a small works, even one subject to a fluctuating load, can meet common effluent standards. If no maintenance is carried out no works of any size will provide any real treatment over a long period of time.

References

[1] *Operation and Management of small Sewage Works,* Min. Housing and Local Government, H.M.S.O., London, 1965.

[2] *Safety in Sewers and at Sewage Works,* Inst. Civ. Eng., H.M.S.O., London, 1969.

15 Comparison of treatment processes and plant designs

In many cases for the installation of a small sewage works a choice has to be made as to the type of process preferred or required for a given site. Once this choice has been made, the works can be constructed locally or a package plant purchased. It is therefore necessary to compare the overall processes and individual methods and to ensure that valid comparisons are made between the range of processes and designs available. The plant of lowest capital cost may not necessarily fulfil the requirements of effluent quality or site conditions. Besides general discussions of the relative merits of the processes, three examples are reviewed.

15.1 Requirements of treatment works

It is assumed that plants are expected to meet the common 20 : 30 Royal Commission standard and that any tertiary treatment process can be added to the process. The likely factors which will influence the choice of a plant are shown in Table 15.1. For a package plant unit additional data should be

Table 15.1   *Requirements of any process to meet 20 : 30 Royal Commission effluent standard and likely local restrictions*

Capital cost
Annual running cost
Delivery or construction time
Size of plant
Recommended daily, weekly and annual maintenance requirements
Sludge production and frequency of desludging
Head loss through plant
Fly and odour nuisance
Noise levels
Distance to nearest habitation
Start up time and procedure
Weir loadings
Hydraulic velocities in settlement tank
Retention times

requested to ensure that comparisons are made on a similar basis – Table 15.2.

Certain of the requirements outlined in Table 15.1 are obvious and generally applicable to all sites e.g. capital costs, delivery time. The relative importance of many of the other factors is often very dependent upon local conditions. At small works where little skilled supervision is available, commitments of manpower and maintenance requirements can assume great importance. Different types of plant present different advantages and disadvantages, while package plants can be designed to different demands. Percolating filters usually have associated fly nuisance but are quieter than small activated sludge plants.

In choosing between the various quotations for package plants and making comparisons with locally constructed plants, it is vital to compare quotations based upon the same data. The additional points given in Table 15.2 should therefore be considered to check the loading figures and any ancillary requirements for the purchaser.

Table 15.2   *Additional requirements for package plant specifications*

Population figures used in specification
Flow, B.O.D. and S.S. values used in specification
Construction requirements prior to delivery of units
Installation and commissioning agreements
Additional costs prior to commissioning

15.2   Comparison of treatment methods

Four main options are usually available to the engineer responsible for the installation of a small sewage treatment plant:–

1) Design and construct a small percolating filter sewage works to conform with CP 302: 1972 or similar principles.
2) Design and construct a small activated sludge sewage works to conform with CP 302: 1972 or similar principles.
3) Purchase and install an activated sludge package plant.
4) Purchase and install a rotating disc package plant.

Other options are available; e.g. percolating filter plants are available from 'package plant' manufacturers. Septic tanks can still meet the standards imposed for very small isolated communities.

A few general points apply to most situations and these points should be considered for each case. In terms of capital costs, a rotating disc package plant will be up to twice the cost of an extended aeration package plant. A percolating filter plant usually costs more to construct than an activated sludge plant. Comparisons between the effective capital cost of package plants and locally constructed plants usually depends greatly upon local conditions – availability of materials, labour, skilled design and supervision. The decisions between all types of plant are often more dependent upon factors other than capital cost for small works. Factors like noise, size, access, head loss, maintenance and availability of electrical supplies can seriously prejudice one type of plant in given circumstances, even if the cost of construction is low.

The electrical running costs of activated sludge plants are usually higher than for other systems. This is particularly so for coarse bubble aerated systems which consume the most energy. Oxidation ditch systems consume less electrical power than other activated sludge systems, while rotating disc plants use very small amounts of electrical power ($\sim$20% of that required by diffused air activated sludge plants). Provided that the site can provide sufficient head difference and no pumping is required, a percolating filter can be operated by gravity and consume no electrical power. Similarly, a septic tank does not require electrical power.

All types of activated sludge and percolating filter plants require daily maintenance to ensure effective operation. Activated sludge package with their more compact design should require less attention. Rotating disc plants require minimum attention, usually restricted to the periodic visual inspection which is more usually associated with septic tank installations. Account should therefore be taken of the long term (20 year) cost of labour and electricity when assessing the total cost of plants.

The land area required for a percolating filter works is approximately twice that required for a separate tank system activated sludge plant. Rotating disc and package activated sludge plants are more compact, requiring approximately a quarter of the area required for a percolating filter works.

Percolating filters are generally silent apart from the dosing or tipping mechanism. The loud erratic noise of a tipping trough can disturb the sleep of campers and be a source of aggravation and complaint. There is, however, considerable fly and sometimes odour nuisance associated with percolating filters together with considerable head loss. Activated sludge plants have little head loss and have little fly and odour nuisance, although wind-blown foam and airborne bacterial suspensions can create some difficulties. The latter can usually be overcome with screening by fencing or bushes. These are often required in many cases to hide the plant for aesthetic and safety reasons. The aeration mechanism for activated sludge plants does create a significant amount of noise. Even after sound-proofing a motor or compressor house, the noise level may still significantly limit the siting of plants. Rotating disc plants are very quiet and have no associated fly and odour nuisance and little head loss. These plants are installed complete with covers, usually as a safety precaution to prevent damage to the discs and to prevent possible accidents if persons are dragged under the liquid by the discs. The resulting works is therefore aesthetically acceptable.

All types of biological treatment processes require some acclimatization to a new sewage or during start up conditions. Careful management is necessary to ensure effective accumulation of viable micro-organisms, particularly if extreme loads are anticipated. With careful control, all of the biological processes can be adjusted to accommodate some degree of fluctuation and increase of load.

Hydraulic wash out of biological materials is more likely in activated sludge plants than in plants where the biological materials are attached to solid supports.

These generalized points, together with all local conditions and restraints, need to be considered along with the type of outline descriptions given for possible treatment processes. Three relevant communities are discussed: isolated cottages, a small village and a camping and caravan site. It is not possible to recommend one definite general solution to any of these situations; instead the general design features of each will be outlined and comparisons made between relevant options.

15.3   Isolated cottages

Two adjacent cottages in an isolated position require sewage treatment to meet an effluent standard of less than 100 mg/l suspended solids. One cottage is permanently occupied and has three occupants. The other cottage is a holiday home which is occupied during the summer months and for limited periods (weekends) during the rest of the year; there are usually five occupants. The holiday home is equipped with a garbage grinder; both cottages have running water. The treatment process should deal with the sewage generated by eight persons.

For such a situation effective settlement will usually fulfil the required conditions. The choice is therefore usually between a septic tank — usually to be built by a local builder — or purchase of a prefabricated settlement unit.

15.3.1   Septic tank

The total capacity of a septic tank as stated in CP 302: 1972 is given by

Capacity = (180 x Population served + 2000) l with an additional 70 l/cap. for garbage grinders.

Capacity of Septic Tank for Isolated Cottages
= (180 x 8 + 2000) l + (70 x 5) l
= 3790 l

This total capacity should be divided into two compartments, the first compartment twice the capacity of the second compartment — first compartment 2520 l, second compartment 1260 l. As the minimum depth of liquid in a septic tank should be 1.5 m, the dimensions of the first tank could be chosen as 1.6 m deep, 1.8 m long and 0.9 m wide with the second tank 1.6 m deep, 0.9 m long and 0.9 m wide. It is therefore convenient to consider the tanks as 1.6 m x 2 m x 1 m and 1.6 m x 1 m x 1 m. It is important to realize that these sizes refer to the volume occupied by the liquids and that additional space (0.5 m) is required above the liquid surface. The tank would probably require annual desludging and probably require one tanker load.

For such relatively small tanks, level floors are usually standard. The two tanks can be separate tanks or combined tanks; the combined tank system is often the cheapest to construct. The positions of inlet and outlet pipes and of interconnection are described in CP 302: 1972, together with suggestions for access, ventilation and cover. The floor of the tank is usually constructed of concrete and the walls of suitably rendered brickwork, concrete or prefabricated blocks. The tank should clearly be watertight and have the strength to withstand the weight of liquid contained and any external forces.

15.3.2 Construction of the septic tanks
For such small tanks, level floors are adequate and the two tanks can be built separately or as a combined tank. The combined tank in this case would be cheaper to construct. The analysis of the tanks would be carried out as described in Section 12.2.2. and on that basis wall thicknesses of 350 mm (13.5 inches) for the longitudinal walls, and 250 mm (9 inches) for the transverse walls would be adequate. The loading on the floor of the tank is light and the thickness of the base would be governed by constructional rather than strength requirements. A floor slab thickness of 150 mm would be provided, with a light mesh of steel reinforcement to satisfy the minimum requirements of CP 2007.

The position of inlet and outlet pipes and of interconnections is described in CP 302: 1972, together with suggestions for access, ventilation and cover.

Assuming the material and labour costs as detailed in Table 15.3, it is estimated that the cost of this tank, excluding pipe work, would be approximately £550.

15.3.3 Settlement units
Prefabricated settlement units can be purchased direct from manufacturers and are sometimes available from builders' merchants. These tanks perform a similar function to septic tanks — settlement of solids and some anaerobic digestion. The tanks require regular desludging and the effluent quality is similar to that

Table 15.3   *Approximate rates for quantities in the civil engineering works (1975–1976).*

Excavate to foundation level	£3.00 per m^3
Supply and lay hardcore subgrade	£5.50 per m^3
Reinforced concrete floor, including steel	£27.00 per m^3
Shuttering — External shuttering	£13.00 per m^2
— Internal shuttering	£15.00 per m^2
Curved shuttering	£22.00 per m^2
Reinforced concrete walls including steel	£43.00 per m^3
Reinforced concrete cover slabs	£35.00 per m^3
Supply and lay engineering brick — $13\frac{1}{2}$ in thick	£17.20 per m^2
9 in thick	£14.00 per m^2
Waterproof cement rendering to brick work	£2.70 per m^2

from septic tanks. The units are often made from fibreglass and are spherical, (Fig. 15.1). A plant to treat the liquids from the isolated cottages would have a capacity of approximately 4.5 m^3 and would cost approximately £300 (1976) ex works. Additional expense is involved in delivery, V.A.T., excavation of a suitable hole, provision of a base and perhaps backfill, connection to the sewer and disposal of the effluent. The capital cost of the units and the provision of a base and backfill depends upon drain invert depths and ground conditions. Dry conditions and small drain invert depths mean that light weight units can be purchased; provision of a 0.1 m concrete base usually suffices and the units can be backfilled with any fine material. Wet ground conditions necessitate heavy duty tanks, a thicker polythene film sealed base, backfilling with concrete and extra care to avoid flotation. As with the septic tank effluents, final discharge would be to a convenient water course or by surface irrigation. The length of the irrigation drains is usually dictated by the subsoil porosity which can be ascertained by absorption tests.

The performance and operation of these plants and of septic tanks is comparable. The choice between them must therefore be made on the basis of local construction costs, site location and site size.

15.3.4   Other treatment methods

Two other possibilities can be considered: installation of a cesspool and full biological treatment.

A cesspool is usually constructed to ensure 45 days retention at D.W.F. and minimum liquid loss. For a flow of 180 l/cap. d and the population of 8 persons, this represents a total capacity of 64.8 m^3 — a tank approximately 4 m deep and 4.5 m diameter. The cost of constructing a watertight tank of such dimensions or of just purchasing a prefabricated fibreglass tank is prohibitively expensive. A fibreglass tank of 36 m^3 capacity would cost in excess of £1000. The cesspool will require additional significant expense of regular emptying. The large size of

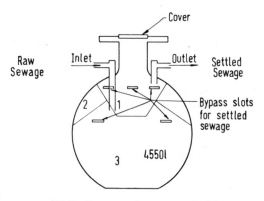

15.1   3 Compartment 4550 litres settlement tank (Klargester Environmental Eng. Ltd.)

the tank will mean that several tanker loads will be required to empty the tank, and this associated running cost will be significant. N.B. The depth must not exceed 4.5 m and hard standing for tankers is required to within approximately 30 m.

Biological treatment is not required to meet the standards described in this case. It is, however, constructive to consider the possible alternatives which could produce effluents to meet 20 : 30 standards. The capital costs of the various possible treatment methods are very similar and often show greater similarity than for larger works. Conventional activated sludge plants are not generally recommended for such small populations due to the problems of shock loadings and intermittent flows. The most suitable biological treatment processes are rotating disc plants and hybrid processes which include activated sludge and a filtration mechanism.

The cost of a small rotating biological filter plant to treat domestic sewage from 8 persons would be £1295 (Klargester) ex works, plus the associated delivery, V.A.T. and installation. Hybrid biological small units are of similar price (£1250) ex works for a C.J.B. Clearwell system. This system again has the associated delivery, V.A.T. and installation charges. Both systems require an electrical supply and some maintenance and desludging which can be obtained on a contract basis. The Clearwell system will require extra installation work in siting and installing the air compressor and control systems, and will consume more electrical power and generate more noise than the rotating disc system. Both systems should provide good quality effluents and be visually acceptable.

15.4 Small community

A small community in southern Scotland contains 70 private 3 and 4 bedroom detached and semi-detached houses. Land is available for a small sewage works in a field adjacent to a burn (small stream) which is to be used to receive the final effluent. The field has a considerable gradient, between 1 in 20 and 1 in 10. Soil conditions are not expected to be difficult.

The likely population of such an estate would be in middle income brackets and average about $3\frac{1}{2}$ persons per house – total population 245 persons. Water consumption would be higher than the British average (middle income and Scottish) – 250 l/d for each inhabitant. The B.O.D.$_5$ is likely to be 0.055 kg/cap. d (220 mg/l). Thus the total D.W.F. flow would be 61 250 l/d, with a total B.O.D.$_5$ of 13.5 kg/d.

For such a community the local River Purification Board is likely to adopt Royal Commission 20 : 30 standards for the effluent. The major option which remains concerns the volume of sewage to be treated. This restriction is a matter for discussion between the River Purification Board and likely installers. Local conditions usually impose restrictions upon effluent discharges and these will be accounted for in the standards set. Exact interpretation of the standards is usually the basis for some dialogue between the River Purification Board and suppliers or purchasers (e.g. acceptance of a unit which will normally meet standards but under extreme conditions may fail, or possible modification of the standards in the light of quoted prices for a particular site).

For this type of community three conditions are likely; the choice between the possible conditions usually depends mainly upon the type and state of the sewerage system and the dilution available in the receiving stream.

a) If only foul water is to be treated – a separate sewerage system – the treatment plant could be designed as described in CP 302: 1972. All of the foul water would pass through the treatment works while surface water would pass through a screen and be discharged directly. It is important to stress that CP 302: 1972 only applies to the treatment of sewage which is not diluted by surface water and that these conditions are the only ones for which this Code of Practice can be used.

b) If the sewerage system is partially combined, or receives considerable volumes of infiltration water, and/or if dilution factors in the receiving water are small, 3 D.W.F. would require full biological treatment. Volumes between 3 and 6 D.W.F. would be screened and settled in storm water tanks. The settled storm water would then be discharged or preferably passed through the treatment plant. Flows in excess of 6 D.W.F. could be screened and discharged directly to the receiving water. This type of standard is commonly imposed on the discharge from large scale municipal works.

c) For combined sewerage systems and/or sewerage systems which suffer from considerable infiltration and/or for receiving waters with very small dilution factors, flows up to 6 D.W.F. would require full biological treatment. Flows in excess of 6 D.W.F. could be discharged after screening or with some settlement. Under certain sets of conditions the standards may require full treatment for flows greater than 6 D.W.F., e.g. 8 D.W.F.; such restrictions are usually a result of local factors, e.g. small dilutions and large populations.

It is instructive to consider the cases a) and c);

In all cases biological treatment is necessary and the possible alternatives are
  i)   Percolating filter locally constructed
  ii) Activated sludge plant locally constructed
  iii) Activated sludge package plant
  iv) Rotating disc package plant.

15.4.1   Treatment of sewage from a separate sewage system

The peak flows described in chapter 4 are likely to be observed in this case. The gradient of the sewers leading to the sewage works means that little flow adjustment can occur in the sewers and any flow maxima will be transmitted directly to the works.

Percolating Filter   Before sewage can be dosed onto a percolating filter, it is necessary to carry out a settlement process. The settled sewage will impose a smaller load upon the biological system and be less likely to block the passage of liquid through the filter bed. As this community is relatively large and will have significant lengths of sewer, some infiltration into the sewers is likely. It is therefore prudent to provide some spare capacity, particularly in the settlement units, to account for the higher volume due to infiltration. For small populations for which only small sewerage systems are required, additional capacity should not be required. In this case the design population is close to the limit of a maximum population of about 300 persons set in CP 302: 1972. The code is only relevant to the treatment of a totally separate sewerage system, so minor modification is desirable.

Two methods of primary settlement for the raw sewage are possible before it is distributed onto the biological filter – a settlement tank or a septic tank.

A septic tank would be designed in accordance with the principles described previously, except that the design capacity would be increased to account for the higher sewage flows (250 l/cap. d instead of the average 180 l/cap. d).

Capacity = (250 x Population Served + 2000) l. This represents a total capacity of 63.2 m^3. For populations in excess of 60 it is suggested that the septic tanks be duplicated – in this case a suitable size for each tank would be 36 m^3. For populations in excess of 100 persons two single compartment tanks in parallel can be employed. A slope of 1 in 4 on the tank floor is preferable. It is however probably preferable to construct two compartment tanks; e.g. the first compartment would be 2.5 m wide by 5.0 m long with a depth sloping from 3.0 m at the inlet to 1.75 m at the outlet; the second compartment would be 2.5 m square and 1.75 m deep. The constructional details would be as for the previous case. It is unlikely that these larger tanks would be constructed in brickwork; concrete construction would be more suitable.

Settlement tanks can be designed as horizontal flow tanks or upward flow tanks. The latter type are often considered to be less suitable for small works and usually necessitate more specialist advice on aspects of design, construction and operation.

The total capacity of a horizontal flow tank is taken as the greater of either 100 l/cap. or 15 h retention at D.W.F. – in this case the latter – 38.4 m^3. Such a tank could be in the form of one tank 2.7 m wide by 8.1 m long and sloping from 2.3 m deep at the inlet to 1.5 m deep at the outlet. It is usually recommended that the provision of duplicate tanks considerably eases maintenance. Two smaller tanks 2 m wide by 6 m long and sloping from 2.1 m deep at the inlet to 1.5 m deep at the outlet would be preferred. Neither of these designs exceeds the maximum weir overflow rate of 200 m^3/md.

The choice between the septic tanks and the settlement tanks would be made on the basis of constructional costs and the availability of labour for maintenance, particularly desludging. For this size of community the settlement tanks are probably preferable, while smaller sites would favour septic tanks. The inclusion of automatic scraper mechanisms even on small tanks is more likely to be economically viable as the cost of labour increases.

Small scraper mechanisms are available even for tanks of this small size.

Robert Hudson (Leeds) can supply hand or motor operated machines for a capital cost of £2000–£2500 (1976). The machine consists of a compound beam to which a rubber blade is attached. This is mounted on bogies which run on rails extending the length of the tank. The machine is operated by means of a wire rope and haulage unit which can be a manual winch or an electric motor with reduction gear.

More common scraper mechanisms are only usually available for larger sized tanks, 10 m minimum width or 5 m diameter for a circular tank. In all cases the proportional costs are very high for small tanks, as much of the equipment is common to all sizes (motors, bearings, end carriage).

The volume of the percolating filter for this size of population is calculated at 0.6 m^3/cap. d i.e. 147 m^3; thus for a depth of 1.8 m the surface area would be 81.6 m^2. This can be achieved by one filter of 11 m diameter or 2 filters of 8 m diameter. Again the single filter will be cheaper to construct although the provision of two filters permits greater flexibility, and the possibility of employing alternating double filtration to accommodate increased loads. The additional costs of providing two small filters is unlikely to be justified and, at the risk of underloading the filter, a single filter would probably be chosen.

The distribution system for biological filters of this type would be from a rotating distributor with four arms in a cruciform configuration: the central column would have a bore size of 100 mm, while the arms would be 50 mm bore. The supply cost of this equipment (including supervision of erection) would be £750 (William E. Farrer Ltd). Equipment for the two smaller filters would be similar and cost only slightly less per filter – almost double the total cost. The settled sewage will require to be dosed onto the filter through a dosing chamber and dosing syphon – Chapter 8. The dosing chamber capacity is usually calculated at $3–5$ l/m^2 of filter area, i.e. 0.5 m^3. The depth of draught in the dosing chamber should be 225 mm and the hydraulic head measured between the surface of the media and the top water level should be between 540 mm and 610 mm. The cost of the dosing syphon would be approximately £85 (William E. Farrer); construction of the dosing chamber and installation would be additional.

The capacity of the final settlement tank for conditions of no surface water in the sewage is given in CP 302: 1972 as

$$\text{Capacity} = (30 \times \text{Population Served} + 1500)\ l$$

This formula is based upon 4 hours retention at D.W.F., therefore for this community with high per capita flows, the formula would be modified to

$$\text{Capacity} = (40 \times \text{population served} + 1500)\ l$$
$$= 11.3\ m^3$$

The horizontal flow settlement tanks would be constructed as for the primary tanks with a total capacity of approximately 15 m^3 to allow for the inclusion of some infiltration water.

The total plant would therefore probably include: screens, duplicate primary settlement tanks, dosing chamber and syphon, final settlement and facilities for discharge of the final effluent. Recirculation and tertiary treatment should not be required. However, irrigation of the effluent over a grass plot or construction of a sand or pebble bed filter would be likely choices for tertiary treatment. The choice would depend upon local rainfall, soil conditions, site gradient, labour and costs.

The analysis and design of the various alternatives for the three stages of the treatment would be carried out according to the methods detailed in Section 12.2.2. With the sizes of tanks in this example, it would be uneconomical to use brickwork and reinforced concrete would be more suitable. However, since the tanks are still relatively small, the thickness of the walls and bases would be determined from constructional rather than strength requirements. In all tanks, the wall and floor thicknesses would be 150 mm with steel reinforcement in both faces. The tanks would be built on a solid foundation with a minimum of 150 mm of well compacted hardcore for a sub-base. Using the costs detailed in Table 15.3, the estimated costs of the various alternatives, excluding the costs of pipework and machinery, are given in Table 15.4. It is interesting to note that it is often cheaper to build two smaller rectangular tanks than a single larger one, whereas it is cheaper to build a single large circular tank than two small circular tanks. The estimated minimum costs of the system would be £11 130.

These costs only refer to the costs of constructing the actual tanks. Additional expense will be involved in constructing certain of the smaller or more detailed units, e.g. dosing chamber, ventilation for the percolating filter and for media. Other costs will include associated pipeworks and mechanical equipment. The total cost is therefore likely to be near to £18 000.

Extended aeration activated sludge plant   It is unlikely that a small activated sludge plant would be constructed locally to serve this size of community. The necessity for specialist design, construction and maintenance would preclude local construction. The general design criteria for the plants should be met by package activated sludge plants and it is therefore worthwhile to consider the

Table 15.4   *Estimated costs for the principal civil engineering works (1975–1976)*

Septic tank		£3950
Primary settlement tank	Single settlement tank	£3850
	Double settlement tank	£3150
Percolating filter	Single tank	£6410
	Double tank	£8780
Final settlement tank	Double tank	£1570

approximate sizes required. Screened sewage would pass directly into the aeration unit. The retention time in this unit should be greater than 24 hours, therefore the design figure of 230 l/cap. recommended in CP 302: 1972 should be increased to 320 l/cap. The total capacity of the aeration unit is therefore 78.4 m^3. To allow for some infiltration, the total volume could be increased slightly. For tanks 3 m deep, this represents a total surface area of approximately 30 m^2. The tanks (if 3 m deep) would be aerated from a compressor of minimum duty capacity of 2500 m^3 of air per day. A standby compressor of similar capacity would also be required.

The size of the subsequent settlement unit should be similar to that outlined for the percolating filter installation, i.e. 15 m^3. Such a size will be within any possible limitation on surface loading (22 m^3/m^{2}d or weir loadings (200 m^3/md).

Activated sludge package plants   A commercially manufactured unit is likely to be cheaper and more easily commissioned and maintained than a locally constructed small extended aeration plant for this community. The cost of a small plant to serve this community is likely to be between £10 000 and £20 000 plus the cost of constructing a concrete base slab and installation. The plant would cost approximately £250 per year (1976) for electricity. The units will require desludging as will all of the other treatment processes. The volume of sludge and the frequency of desludging will depend upon the particular plant and the sewage treated. Desludging is likely at intervals of approximately every 6 weeks, with the removal of approximately 10 m^3 of sludge.

In all cases it is preferable if some check is made on the sizes and geometry of the plants suggested by different companies. Simple extended aeration plants which include only an aeration unit and a settlement unit should conform to the general principles of CP 302: 1972. The total volumes of the aeration and settlement chambers, together with the aeration capacity, standby compressor capacity, surface loading and weir loading rates on the settlement tanks, can be checked and compared. For cases which do not specify sewage volumes or strengths, these design loadings should be compared. If the design for this community were based upon 150 l/cap. d, the size and cost of the plant would be lower. If reliable figures are not available, discussion with manufacturers is often useful. Reputable manufacturers have considerable experience in sizing treatment plant capacity and can usually offer advice on loading factors.

Exact comparisons have to be made between processes which employ the same treatment process. Units which utilise separate aerobic sludge digestion will have a smaller aeration chamber than those which employ simple extended aeration (approximately 50% less). The lower volume in the aeration chamber is supplemented by a separate aerobic digester and the lower sludge concentration in the settlement tank makes sludge wash out less likely. Direct comparison between the capacities of plants with and without separate aerobic digesters is more difficult. Comparisons have to be made between the relevant factors, e.g.

provision of standby capacity as a percentage of total capacity, settlement loading rates relative to likely loads and flows to the settlement tanks.

Consideration should also be taken of the general geometry and flow patterns through the plants and the implications in terms of efficiency and labour. The provision of adequate flow balancing devices, to ensure that surge flows are not imposed upon the plant, scum pumps to remove or recycle fats and scum, and effective devices for control of the air flow, are all factors which will tend to improve the plant and may not be included in all units. The aeration chamber should provide adequate aeration, adequate mixing and prevent short circuiting of sewage directly into the settlement unit. Again, therefore, plants whose geometry includes adequate baffles and weirs should ensure effective treatment. Failure of the settlement processes is the most common single major cause of poor quality effluents from small extended aeration plants. Besides the provision of sufficient total volume, the settlement unit should provide the optimum conditions for the settlement process, i.e. little turbulence. It is therefore instructive to examine the inlet to the settlement unit and to assess the ability of the inlet device for producing a non turbulent flow. Adjustable airlift or electrically driven pumps for the transfer of liquid into the settlement zone and for the return of sludge, are usually provided on larger extended aeration package plants. Small plants which rely upon hydraulic and gravity flow into and out of the settlement zone are very prone to sludge wash out from the settlement zone during periods of high hydraulic flow. The advantages of positive pumping have therefore to be judged in relation to the likelihood of hydraulic loads at a particular plant.

All of the extended aeration package plants marketed by reputable manufacturers are usually capable of meeting 20 : 30 effluent standards, provided that the design conditions are approximately correct. The plants do, however, require adequate maintenance — desludging, degreasing, cleaning screens etc., and the inclusion in a plant of any devices likely to minimize these maintenance operations is advantageous.

Rotating biological filter package plants   Rotating biological filter plants are normally only available as a complete unit from a manufacturer. The general design and principles of operation are very similar to those of a percolating filter. Settled sewage comes into contact with an aerobic growing medium which is attached to an inert support material, the biological floc which shears off from the support is settled and the effluent discharged. The sizes of the settlement units should follow the general guidelines established for the other types of plant. The primary settlement zone often acts as a septic tank and consequently has provision for the bulk of sludge storage. The disc area required is estimated from the general design/performance data available on rotating disc plants. The calculation depends upon the B.O.D.$_5$ applied to the disc system and the hydraulic flow to the plant. In this case the total hydraulic flow is approximately $65 \, m^3/d$ with a raw sewage strength of $220 \, mg/l$. The settled sewage would have a B.O.D.$_5$ of perhaps 150 mg/l and would require a reduction of at least 87% to reach a 20 mg/l effluent standard. For this size of community, this represents a total minimum disc area of approximately 1000 m^2, e.g. 160 discs of 2 m diameter or 70 discs of 3 m diameter. The discs would be arranged in series. As with the previous processes, the high flows create a need for additional capacity.

The plants are usually designed to minimize maintenance attention (1 hour/week) and power consumption (2000 kWh per year, $\sim$ £40 – 1976) and require desludging at intervals of approximately 4 or 6 months. The only additional requirement would be the provision of a suitable base to meet the local ground conditions.

15.4.2   Treatment of sewage from a combined sewerage system

Sewage from a combined sewerage system will require some form of flow splitting to prevent very high prolonged peak flows from entering the plant. This usually takes the form of a side weir constructed so that only a maximum flow of approximately 6 D.W.F. (or greater) passes to the sewage works. This can mean that the treatment plant is more likely to receive a more even, if higher, rate of flow throughout the 24 hour period compared to the separate system. The excess storm water is usually discharged directly to the water course with a minimum of treatment, usually only screening. The provision of storm water tanks would not be feasible at a community of this small size, unless adequate provision could be made for their management. In certain cases it is possible to provide some settlement by providing a tank with automatic pumping facilities which will take excess flows and automatically pump sewage back to the sewage works at time of lower flows. Manufacturers can often suggest suitable arrangements.

Normally, plants are merely designed to account for the higher, more prolonged peak flows due to the presence of storm water in the sewage. The designs according to CP 302: 1972 include significant overcapacity to accommodate peak flows; provided, therefore, that the weir works effectively, the general sizes of the previous sections can be utilised. This does necessitate ensuring that the weirs do not become blocked, which can occur with the higher concentration of extraneous material present during the first flush of a storm.

In general, septic tanks are less suitable for treating higher hydraulic flows than settlement tanks. Particularly if there is a high accumulation of sludge in the tank, prolonged high flows will wash out the anaerobic sludge. The lower level of sludges in a settlement tank make it less likely that very poor effluents will occur. The sizes of the percolating filters, rotating biological filters, and the activated sludge units, which are mainly designed on the basis of B.O.D. load, again should be sufficient to treat the combined sewage. The shorter retention in the activated sludge unit should not affect treatment efficiency and, as the amount of aerobic sludge digestion is not usually very great, little difference should occur. Biological filter processes do not suffer from significant losses of

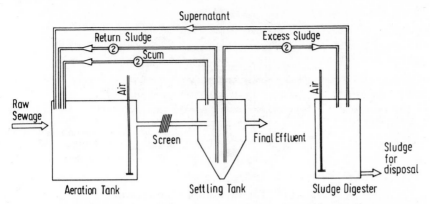

15.2 Diagrammatic representation of flow through Inka Bioreactor.

biomass during periods for higher flow, so poor treatment is unlikely. The major changes that are relevant are in the final settlement tank. The final settlement tank at a sewage works is usually designed on the basis of $1\frac{1}{2}-2$ h retention at peak flows; in this case a volume of 31 m^3.

15.4.3   Inka Bioreactor package plant

A. Johnson Construction Company (Glasgow) have outlined a package plant to serve this community. The plant would be an Inka Bioreactor type 3 DBST unit and would cost £13 000 (1976) plus the cost of providing the necessary concrete base slab. A flow diagram of the plant (Fig. 15.2) and views of the plant (Fig. 15.3) illustrate the general arrangements of the plant. The plant dimensions are 5.5 m diameter and 3.5 m overall depth.

Unscreened sewage passes into a series of deeply baffled aeration units which are aerated through coarse bubble aerators. The sewage passes through a screen into a settlement tank from which sludge is withdrawn, usually once or twice a day, and passed to the aeration unit and to a separate aerobic digester/thickening unit. Supernatant from the settlement tank is discharged as

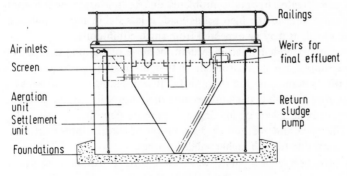

15.3(a)   Side-view of Inka Bioreactor.

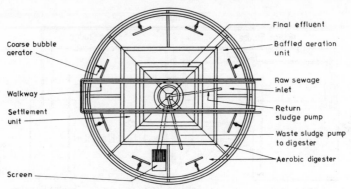

Coarse bubble aerator

Walkway

Settlement unit

Screen

Final effluent

Baffled aeration unit

Raw sewage inlet

Return sludge pump

Waste sludge pump to digester

Aerobic digester

15.3(b)   Top-view of Inka Bioreactor.

final effluent. The plant is supplied with an intermittent automatic scum pump to remove scum from the surface of the settlement tank and return it to the aeration units. Control of the M.L.S.S. is possible by adjustment of the frequency, flow and/or duration of pumping settled sludge into the sludge digester or as return activated sludge back into the aeration units. Once set, these sludge pumps should maintain a constant M.L.S.S. in the aeration unit and prevent overloading the settlement tank. The aerobic digester is also automatically controlled to permit return of supernatant liquids to the aeration unit, usually on a daily basis.

The treatment plant is, essentially, an extended aeration plant, although it does not necessarily conform to the loading capacities within CP 302. The design called for in CP 302 generally considers the case where mineralization is attempted within the aeration basin which, therefore, means that the aeration tank and settling tank carry a combined 'high' sludge loading. This, in turn, can lead to other problems because the solids loading of sludge within the system in relation to substrate level is too high. Surface loading on the settling tank becomes a problem due to hindered settling velocity effects. Sludge removal by direct sludge withdrawal from either the base of the settling tank or the aeration system also creates hydraulic problems due to the associated flushing action. Such a plant, due to the high solids load, is less stable under conditions of peak hydraulic load, as may be expected from small communities.

In a pure extended aeration system, because of the points raised above, the aeration supply can be a problem in that the higher the solids loading carried within the system, then the more difficult will mixing prove to be, as the higher concentration of solids per unit volume of liquor will require greater energy in order to provide adequate mixing and prevent deposition within the aeration basis. The type and method of distribution of air distributor/diffuser becomes more critical due to such higher solids loadings.

The provision of a separate waste sludge treatment unit, as detailed in the Inka Bioreactor System, provides a facility for aerobic sludge digestion and thickening without any of the attendant problems previously described. Such a unit can also be used 'to control' the mixed liquor solids concentration and thus equate the mixed liquor solids load to the substrate level.

Retention times in the aeration unit are approximately 18 hours at D.W.F. and 3 hours at 6 D.W.F. The compressors are capable of supplying 36 kg of oxygen per day – approximately 4200 m^3/d (cf. Section 15.4.1) and can be run at high speeds to accommodate high load conditions. The surface area of the settlement tank is 9 m^2 for a water depth of 3 m. This corresponds to a surface loading of 0.28 m^3/m^2h at D.W.F. and 1.7 m^3/m^2h at 6 D.W.F. and is designed for upward settling velocities of 0.7–0.85 m/h at 3 D.W.F.

The volume of the settlement tank is slightly larger than that specified in CP 302: 1972. The settlement characteristics should be good because long retention times and associated sludge bulking problems are not possible with the continuous sludge wastage of the digester. The additional size should reduce the possibility of hydraulic wash out at peak flows. The plant is supplied with double sided inboard weirs which mean low weir loadings and an even distribution of final effluent from the tank. The aerobic digester/thickening unit is 15 m^3 and should only require desludging at approximately 50 day intervals. The long retention time in the separate digester is possible because of the return of supernatant liquids and permits the accumulation of a dense, compact, well stabilized sludge ($\sim$ 3% dry solids) with no odour problems.

Once the plant is properly commissioned, it should require relatively little maintenance by comparison with normal extended aeration activated sludge plants (4 hours/week). Descreening should be less than normal because the screen is placed after the aeration unit and therefore less likely to block. Similarly, the inclusion of an automatic scum pump should reduce the frequency or extent of fat and grease removal. The automatic nature of the operation and the presence of the separate sludge digester reduce the possibility of hydraulic 'wash out' and reduce the frequency of desludging. The annual running costs are quoted as £220 (1976).

This plant could also treat sewage from a combined sewerage system, provided that a storm discharge weir and/or some form of storm balancing were incorporated. The sizing of the final settlement tank, together with the low concentration of suspended solids in this tank make it suitable for use under these conditions. The plant would probably require extra descreening to remove the extra materials washed out of the sewers during the first flush of storms.

15.4.4 Ames Crosta Biodisc

Ames Crosta Mills (Heywood, Lancs.) have outlined a rotating biological filter which they market as the Biodisc sewage treatment process. Two of the units are relevant to this community, size 200 which would cost £23 320 (1976) plus the cost of cranage and delivery (£1700), and size 350 which would cost £29 320 (1976) plus delivery and cranage (£2300).

The plants are usually delivered as factory assembled units for installation on a previously prepared concrete base. The raw unscreened sewage passes into a primary settlement zone designed to act as a septic tank. The heavier solids settle out and form an anaerobic sludge (Fig. 15.4). The settled sewage passes into the biological filter unit which consists of a trough divided into several compartments by a series of baffle plates. The baffling causes the sewage to flow in a long, serpentine course through the trough. The discs rotate through the liquid in the trough. The first discs show the largest accumulation of biological material. Slots are provided in the first sections of the trough to allow the fragments which slough off to fall back into the primary settlement zone. The fragments from the later sections are kept in suspension, and are allowed to settle out in a final settlement zone.

The plant is normally enclosed by steel panels (Fig. 15.4) which can be locked to prevent interference. The panels can be removed easily to permit access for desludging the primary septic tank and the final settlement tank. The units normally require desludging two or three times a year.

The size 200 plant contains 90 discs of 3 m diameter mounted in 4 stages, while the size 350 plant contains 158 discs of 3 m diameter mounted in 4 stages. Comparison with the minimum figures given in Section 15.4.1 indicates that the size 200 plant contains sufficient biological capacity and the size 350 should provide good biological treatment. The primary and final tank sizes in the size 200 plant are 30 m^3 and 15.6 m^3, while for the size 350 plant, the tank sizes are 52.4 m^3 and 31.2 m^3 respectively. Comparison with the figures outlined in Section 15.4.1 indicates that there is ample capacity for settlement. The primary tanks will also provide sufficient capacity for sludge storage and some anaerobic digestion. The problems of high per capita flows are again illustrated by these problems of tank sizing.

Ames Crosta recommend the size 200 plant to treat a B.O.D.$_5$ of 13.6 kg/d and an average flow of 36 m^3/d, while the size 350 plant is recommended for B.O.D.$_5$'s of 23.8 kg/d and an average flow of 63 m^3/d. For this community, the B.O.D.$_5$ corresponds almost exactly to that of the size 200 plant, while the excessive flows of sewage exceed the hydraulic design size. The plants are designed to accommodate flows of 6 D.W.F. while still meeting 20 : 30 effluent standards For a community served by a combined sewerage system, the size 350

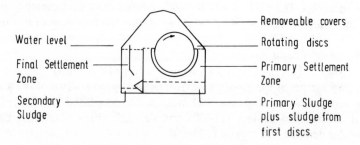

15.4   End-view of Ames Crosta Biodisc.

plant should provide effective treatment at all times. For a community served by a separate sewerage system, a choice has to be made between the size 200 and the size 350 plants. The critical factors will be the incidence of peak flows of moderate duration and the attitudes of the river authorities. This sewage will be received through short sewers which have considerable gradient, therefore high peak flows are to be expected. The plants have been shown to tolerate peak flows of 18 D.W.F. for periods of 20 minutes before the effluent quality deteriorated; for the size 200 plant, this would correspond to flows of 10.5 D.W.F. for periods of 20 minutes for this community. Similarly, the plant could accommodate prolonged flows of 3.5 D.W.F. without deterioration of the effluent below a 20 : 30 effluent standard. The acceptability of the size 200 plant can therefore only be ascertained from a more detailed consideration of the likely flow patterns and by discussion with the river authority. The river authority may accept average 24 hour effluent analysis and tolerate some effluents slightly in excess of the 20 : 30 effluent standard, or may insist upon strict observance of the standard. Detailed discussions between the plant purchaser, the manufacturer and the river authority are required before a choice between the size 200 and size 350 Biodisc can be made for a separate sewage system.

The plant should require a minimum of attention — periodic greasing and inspection, and will consume little electricity, perhaps £40/year. Desludging is likely to be required at intervals of 4 or 6 months. Normally, a contract tanker service is employed. The sludges, particularly the larger volume of sludge from the primary settlement tank, are similar to a septic tank sludge. The final disposal of this sludge should be considered if a tanker service is not feasible. Septic tank sludges are not amenable to direct land spraying and trenching with lime addition can be a malodorous process. The sludges are usually more amenable to mechanical dewatering than waste activated sludges, and can be dewatered at central locations or with mobile equipment.

The plant, therefore, provides a compact, low maintenance, aesthetically acceptable, low running cost installation.

15.5 Camping and caravan site

A small camping and caravan site is planned within an area of great scenic beauty in England. The site is expected to hold 75 caravans and 75 tents. The site would be closed all winter, open at Easter and be 60–100% filled, is under used (10%) until the Spring Holiday (again 60–100% filled), falls to approximately 35% capacity through June, rises to 70–100% in July, effectively 100% in August, 40% September, and closes 1st October until the following Easter. The site is expected to be a 'long stay' site (7 nights) rather than a stop-over site. The site will include a toilet block supplied with hot and cold water, including flush toilets, urinals, wash basins, showers, together with facilities for hand washing clothes. Several stand pipes for cold water supplies will be available. The drains serving the stand pipes are to be connected to the sewage treatment plant. All surface water will be excluded from the sewage treatment plant.

The site is square and the ground flat, sloping off in one corner to a stream which will act as receiving water for the effluent discharge. Separate drainage is expected such that only foul water will be treated by the plant. The Water Authority requires treatment of the sewage such that the effluent meets 10 mg/l. B.O.D.$_5$ and 10 mg/l. S.S. As the size of the site is restricted, the treatment works should occupy the smallest possible area and create the least nuisance to campers.

The treatment works is required to deal with the full flow from a 150 pitch site. At longer stay sites the tents are likely to be larger than average and can be assumed to have 3.5 occupants, i.e. 525 persons. The total per capita B.O.D.$_5$ is likely to be similar or only slightly smaller than other communities, 0.05 kg/d, a total of 26.25 kg/d. However, the flow of sewage is less easily predicted. A site of this nature would have flows below the higher value for the previous community (250 l/d) due to its location (England), lack of full household facilities and the presence of caravans with chemical closets. The per capita flow is likely to be between 100 and 200 l/d; a figure of 140 l/d is probably reasonable in this case.

This camping and caravan site clearly requires separate disposal facilities for the chemical closet wastes which have been assumed to be included in the sewage flow to the treatment plant. The overall designs will be outlined; exact specifications of tank sizes will be similar to the previous example, while specifications of plant division and operation are discussed for the particular package plants.

15.5.1   Primary settlement

Three alternatives are possible for primary settlement tanks: manually or automatically desludged horizontal tanks or radial flow tanks; it is unlikely that septic tanks would be applicable for this larger size of community, although their lack of maintenance does offer some advantage.

Manually desludged primary tanks designed on 15 hours retention at D.W.F. would have a total volume of 45.9 m^3. Automatically desludged primary tanks designed at 8 hours retention at D.W.F. would have a total volume of 24.5 m^3. Radial tanks would have a similar volume to the automatically desludged horizontal tanks.

15.5.2   Biological treatment

A percolating filter would be designed to treat 0.1 kg of applied B.O.D.$_5$/m^3 – a total volume of 183.8 m^3. This could be achieved by two filters of 1.8 m depth and 8 m diameter, or one filter of 11 m diameter. An extended aeration plant without primary settlement designed at 30 hours nominal retention, would have a total volume of 92 m^3. A rotating biological filter for this size of population requires a total disc area of approximately 920 m^2 and could be served by 65 discs of 3 m diameter, with some reduction possible if several shafts could be used.

15.5.3 Final settlement

Final settlement tanks designed to give 2 hours retention at 3 D.W.F. would have a total volume of 18.4 m³.

15.5.4 Tertiary treatment

Three simple methods of tertiary treatment are possible: grass plots, pebble bed clarifiers and slow sand filters. The design of these units depends greatly upon the actual quality of the effluents from the previous treatment plant. For good quality effluents — below the 20 : 30 standard at all times — the following designs are probably over generous.

Grass plots would not normally be considered at this site, as it is specified that only small areas are available. An area of approximately 2 m²/cap. should be sufficient for this community, provided that soil conditions and climate are favourable. This represents a total area of 1050 m². Two plots, each of approximately 500 m², should therefore be constructed and used alternatively. Pebble bed clarifiers to receive 1 m³/m² h at 3 D.W.F. would necessitate a surface area of 9.2 m². Slow sand filters require a larger area, and the size is usually restricted by the limitations of liquid flow through porous media. To accommodate flows at approximately 0.2 m³/m² h, necessitates a surface area of 46 m², and two filters of this size are therefore required.

The capital costs of the pebble bed clarifier and the slow sand filter, and the large land area required for the grass plots usually makes tertiary treatment unrealistic, particularly at a seasonal site.

15.5.5 Satec Diffused Air Plant

Satec (Crewe) have outlined an extended aeration activated sludge plant including a pebble bed clarifier to reach a 20 : 30 effluent standard and an additional upward flow sand filter to meet a 10 : 10 effluent standard. The activated sludge plant would be a Satec 75-B-269 Diffused Air Plant costing £12 980 ex works, with a 30-PC-169 Pebble Bed Clarifier costing £4170, a total cost of £17 150 (1976). To meet the more stringent 10 : 10 effluent standard, an upward flow sand filter would be required with an additional cost of approximately £12 000 (1976).

The Satec diffused air plants are rectangular units which consist of a steel aeration compartment into which is inset a settlement compartment, Fig. 15.5. The overall dimensions of this plant are 8 m long by 7 m wide and 3 m deep. The sewage is aerated from air blowers mounted on the tank and controlled from a control panel. The mixed liquor settles in the settlement compartment and some sludge returns through the small gap in the bottom of this compartment, to maintain adequate concentrations in the aeration compartment.

This plant is likely to be partially buried for aesthetic reasons, and would be supplied with 4—8 kg magnesium anode packs, two to be fitted on each side of the plant and as far from the wall as possible. The plant is supplied with a

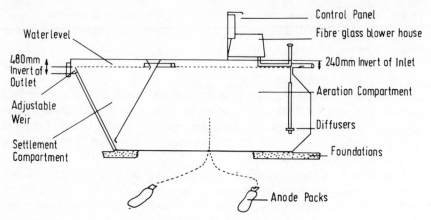

15.5   Satec diffused air extended aeration activated sludge plant.

skimming eductor, baffles and weirs between the aeration and settlement compartments, to minimize turbulence and interference in the settlement compartments. The plant would normally be delivered in two sections, each without one side wall; the sections are off loaded onto a pre-prepared concrete foundation, and bolted together to form a single tank. The plant has an aeration volume of 113 m³ and the surface area of the settlement tank is 17.5 m² − both of which are comparable with the sizes outlined in Sections 15.5.2 and 15.5.3. Large blowers are supplied which will run at 1210 r.p.m. and so would be quieter than a cheaper but faster (2050 r.p.m.) smaller blower.

The upward flow clarifier is supplied in agreement with the 1969 Technical Memorandum and is to ensure effluent standards even under conditions of erratic flow. The upward flow clarifier is a double hopper 6.1 m long, 3.05 m wide and 2 m deep. The unit is again constructed in 6 mm mild steel plate and would be protected by two 8 kg magnesium anode packs. The units are clamped onto pre-prepared concrete foundations. Effluent from the activated sludge plant passes into the bottom of the hopper and up through 15 cm of graded stone (4–6 mm diameter) which is supported on an expanded metal grid. A submersible pump is supplied to remove the sludge which is dislodged from the stones during backwashing, Fig. 15.6. The bed area of the clarifier is 16.9 m² which compares favourably with the minimum figures in Section 15.5.4.

The sand filter, Fig. 15.7, is formally similar to the upward flow clarifier. The liquid passes up through a bed of sand. The sand bed is cleaned on a daily basis by draining the filter and scouring the filter with air while passing a reduced flow of wash water. This forms a surface of water which gradually rises through the sand medium, at the surface of which the air bubbles burst. This rising interface scours the accumulated material from the medium and this is washed away by a subsequent flow of wash water.

It is beyond the scope of this volume to discuss in detail the sizing and flow rating of upward flow sand filters. More specialist advice and more detailed

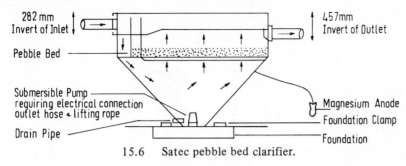

282 mm
Invert of Inlet

457mm
Invert of Outlet

Pebble Bed

Submersible Pump
requiring electrical connection
outlet hose ← lifting rope

Magnesium Anode

Foundation Clamp

Drain Pipe

Foundation

15.6   Satec pebble bed clarifier.

discussion with the supplier should be undertaken by a potential client. This filter is 0.76 m in diameter and has been selected to give an hourly filtration rate of $19.6 \text{ m}^3/\text{m}^2$ with an 8 minute wash at a rate equivalent to $0.72 \text{ m}^3/\text{m}^2$ each minute. In order to finalize such figures, more details would be required because wash rates in particular are temperature dependent. If correctly installed and operated, this should reduce a 20 : 30 effluent to a 10 : 10 effluent.

The activated sludge plant will require daily visits to check the general operation of the plant. This would involve visible inspection and perhaps sampling to check the settlement characteristics of the liquors, and the necessity of desludging. It is also likely that fats and grease which accumulate on the surfaces would require periodic removal, together with any extraneous materials, e.g. rags. The frequency of desludging can only be gauged by observation, as a steady flow of sewage is unlikely at this seasonal site. The upward flow clarifier requires periodic backwashing again, depending upon the flows to the works perhaps once or twice per week. The sand filter requires daily air scouring and backwashing, necessitating a minimum of 2 hours per day. As only one plant can be contemplated, during this period flows cannot pass through the sand filter plant, and provision would be required to store this flow.

The additional capital cost – almost doubling the initial cost and the additional labour commitment – more than doubling the daily time required, illustrate why tertiary treatment is rarely feasible at small sites. In this case the commercial viability of the camping and caravan site would be seriously undermined by these extra costs, and further discussions with the Water Authority would be advisable.

During the start-up of this plant or for periods of low flow, reduced aeration is necessary. The blowers are supplied with a series of pulleys which control the output from the blowers. In this case the blowers should be supplied with a series of pulleys to permit low and variable aeration rates, e.g. 30, 60 and 80% of full capacity. Additionally, a time clock can be installed and for periods of very low flow, the plant would only be aerated for parts of each day – sufficient to maintain aerobic conditions. A more expensive alternative would be to install two duplicate plants of total capacity similar to the previous example, in this case two 38-A-131 plants of total cost £17 580. A smaller single hopper bottom clarifier could then be used – a 27-PC-135 at a cost of £3430. The total cost

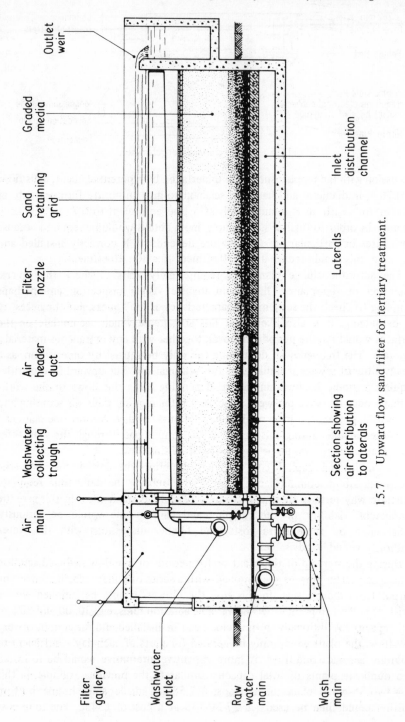

15.7   Upward flow sand filter for tertiary treatment.

would therefore rise to £21 010 but would give the additional flexibility of using one of the plants during times of low flow — probably with less than 100% aeration — and bring the other plant into commission at times of peak flow. This alternative would be more attractive at a site which intended to gradually expand its trade. The initial purchase of one smaller activated sludge plant and the clarifier could be followed by purchase of another activated sludge plant, if the site were found to attract sufficient persons.

15.5.6   C.J.B. Rotating Disc Process

C.J.B. Developments (Portsmouth) have outlined a rotating biological filter to serve this community. The plant would be a Rotating Disc Process Type W Disc Unit, Fig. 15.8 and an upward flow clarifier similar to the previous example Fig. 15.6. The cost of this plant would be as follows:—

Rotating Disc Plant (1976)

	£	
Mechanical Equipment Supply	35,200	
Mechanical Erection	2,350	
Commissioning	750	
Civil Works	16,000	
		£54,300
Tertiary Treatment		
Mechanical Equipment Supply	4,265	
Mechanical Erection	1,200	
Civil Works	600	
		£6,065
TOTAL PLANT COST		£60,365

The unscreened sewage passes into a primary sedimentation/digester tank Fig. 15.8. The tank is designed to act as an Imhoff tank, with the settleable solids falling to the bottom of the unit and not interfering with the normal flow of sewage. Settled sewage passes into the disc stages of the plant. Three disc stages

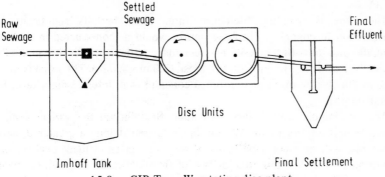

15.8   CJB Type W rotating disc plant.

are included each containing 111 discs of 2 m diameter. The liquor flows through each stage in turn and into a secondary settlement tank, settled sludge is periodically removed by pump and returned to the primary tank for digestion. The clarified effluent overflows and passes to the tertiary treatment stage. Tertiary treatment is achieved by upward flow through a 150 mm deep pebble bed clarifier.

The circular primary settlement unit is constructed in concrete and has an overall depth of 3.85 m and is 4 m in diameter, a total volume of 38 m^3. A steel clarification channel is suspended above the main body of the tank (3.2 m x 1.64 m x 1.6 m as overall depth). The bottom of this clarification channel has sloping sides with an aperture to permit settleable solids to fall into the bulk of the unit, and to prevent gases rising from the digestion zone through the channel.

The 2 m diameter polystyrene discs are mounted on a steel shaft within a glass fibre profiled tank. The use of a total of 333 discs with a total area of 1998 m^2, ensures very effective biological treatment (cf. 15.5.2). Assuming only 30% reduction of B.O.D.$_5$ in the primary unit the actual daily disc loading would be 9.2 g/m^2. The disc stage is designed to reduce the input settled sewage B.O.D.$_5$ from 250 mg/l to 15 mg/l.

Secondary settlement would be in a steel tank 3.55 m square with a hopper base. The total volume of this final clarifier is 18.4 m^3 (cf. Section 15.5.3), with a surface area of 12.3 m^3. A central stilling well is included to reduce the inlet turbulence in this unit.

The steel fabricated pebble bed clarifier is 3.55 m long by 2.6 m wide, area 9.2 m^2 (cf. Section 15.5.4).

Additional equipment includes duty and standby sludge transfer pumps (0.55 kW), a submersible pump for backwashing the pebble bed clarifier (0.55 kW), isolating valves, a control panel with contactors for the discs and pumps and automatic timing mechanisms, with conventional thermal and electrical controls. The control panel and sludge transfer pumps would be housed in a separate free standing kiosk. All of the steel tanks would be protected by two coats of black epoxy resin paint, pipework would be in rigid P.V.C.

The type of rotating biological filter plant permits significant local construction in concrete. The base plinths would be constructed in reinforced concrete, disc units (8.0 m x 4.0 m), secondary settlement unit (4.2 m x 4.2 m), pebble bed clarifier (4.5 m x 2.8 m), kiosk (3.0 m x 2.0 m). The primary Imhoff tank would also be made of reinforced concrete (4 m internal diameter 3.85 m overall depth).

The rotating disc units offer considerable flexibility at this variable load site. The disc unit adjusts to the varying loads, merely taking a greater or smaller active disc area to treat a particular sewage to a given effluent quality. Under condition of low flow only one or two of the units could be used, however, in this case the savings in energy during non use may not warrant the extra pipework involved. During the winter, the plant could be closed down or run with minimal flows to maintain some microbial mass on the discs. Normally this plant would require a maximum start up time of 4 weeks, if partially operative this period would be considerably shorter.

Annual sludge production is estimated as 50 m^3. Normally only the primary tank would be desludged, conveniently at the start of the season. Subsequent desludging would be carried out as required, depending upon site occupancy. Very little maintenance would be required for the biological treatment process, perhaps 1—2 hours per week, mainly general checking, cleaning and inspection. The pebble bed clarifier requires similar additional attention to ensure adequate backwash and continued performance. The power required to drive the disc stages is low, each shaft is driven by a 0.37 kW motor. It is therefore to be anticipated that the approximate weekly power consumption might be 100 kWh.

As in the previous section the requirements of meeting a 10 : 10 effluent standard have greatly increased the costs of the plant. In this case not only has tertiary treatment been installed but the number of rotating discs has been increased to guarantee a high quality effluent passing to the tertiary stage. Less rigorous effluent standards would again reduce the total costs.

For this site this outlined plant should provide a flexible self adjusting treatment works. Although the capital costs are high the electrical running costs and the daily maintenance are low.

15.6   Sludge treatment and disposal

Little discussion of sludge treatment and disposal methods or costs has been included in these case studies. It is important to account for this necessity at any sewage works. For the cases described, the most likely expedient is to employ a tanker service to desludge the tanks and dispose of the sludge. The economics of this service are discussed in Chapter 10. The only site where drying beds may be feasible is the small community, Section 15.4. Provided that suitable land can be purchased, the climate is not grossly unfavourable and adequate labour is available; drying beds could be constructed adjacent to the sewage treatment plant (see Chapters 10 and 14 for details of construction and operation). Even at this site, if some form of package plant is purchased, it is most likely that a tanker service will provide the most acceptable solution.

Suggested further reading

The information used in this chapter has been referred to in the previous chapters and is not requoted. Further information on particular plant or equipment can be obtained from manufacturers' catalogues and descriptive publicity.

16 Sewage treatment in hot climates

This book is concerned primarily with the treatment of sewage from small communities in Britain. While much of the discussion is relevant to other geographical areas, particular circumstances – legal, cultural, technical – dictate modifications of the details of the treatment processes. It is not always feasible to convert directly into other developed practices e.g. North America, nor is it feasible to provide information on all other geographic and climatic locations. Instead, general considerations of sewage treatment in climates hotter than that in Britain will be considered taking examples predominantly from the Middle East. Particular local problems cannot be considered; however the major considerations are similar to those already considered, volume and nature of sewage, unit operations, sludge disposal, and operation and maintenance.

16.1 Volume and nature of sewage

The general discussions in the earlier chapters of the book also apply to other countries. Further limits are imposed by the climate, water supply, drainage and living standards.

In almost all instances the construction of a sewage works is preceded by the installation of a water supply system. Therefore, if accurate figures on sewage flows are not available, water supply figures provide a useful guide. Hot climates will produce a higher demand for water than cooler climates. Thus in conditions which permit adequate water supply, e.g. Southern U.S.A., per capita water supply figures and per capita sewage volumes are high (>400 l/d) and the strength of sewage is low (B.O.D.$_5$ < 170 mg/l). Usually economic strictures prevent this luxurious use of water and volumes are lower. Countries which face severe economic difficulties are therefore likely to have discontinuous water supplies, incomplete distribution systems and are likely to have lower sewage flows and produce stronger sewages (>500 mg/l).

The averaged figures for any country are unlikely to be representative of any one small area. In Britain local variations are less marked as the water distribution system is almost complete and the local water usage variations are not of the same order of magnitude. For communities which are only supplied with communal stand pipes per capita water supply volumes are low 25–70 l/d. In areas of high quality housing the higher temperatures raise domestic per capita water consumption to nearer 300–400 l/d, even in countries which do not have a high per capita income. Between these extreme figures, a range of flows are possible. The amenity value of the area drained will therefore have a considerable effect upon sewage characteristics.

The usual practice when converting water supply figures into sewage volumes is to assume a wastage factor often of approximately 25% to account for distribution losses and water uses which will not result in foul sewage flow. Care has to be taken in making these conversions, particularly for small specialized communities. The use of water for irrigation, particularly lawn sprinkling or for street cleaning, can seriously increase water consumption without influencing the foul sewage; the use of lawn sprinklers can often more than double domestic water consumption. The use of brackish water for certain operations, e.g. to wash cars, can increase sewage flows independent of fresh water supply figures. The nature and state of the sewerage system can therefore influence the sewage. Infiltration of storm water is unlikely to be a problem in much of the Middle East but will be significant during monsoons in India. The connections of fresh and brackish water outlets to drainage systems is much more likely to be a significant factor in hot dry climates.

For a country which has adequate resources to develop a water supply and sewage treatment system, the volumes of water consumed and the volumes and nature of sewage will be similar to those outlined in earlier chapters. It is important to anticipate these changes and to account for them. Per capita water consumption in Kuwait has risen from 57 l/d in 1957 to 145 l/d in 1974. This change has been accompanied by an increase in population of the area served to four times its 1957 value, thus representing an almost 10 fold increase in water supply and sewage flow. The sewage is now similar in strength to that in Britain (Table 16.1) while previously it would have been much stronger. The sewage has similar B.O.D.$_5$ and suspended solids characteristics to British sewage. The major differences are the higher temperature, higher chloride concentration and the presence of significant amounts of hydrogen sulphide in the sewage. The increased sewage temperature reflects the local practice of supplying taps from a roof tank not from the water main, the origin of water from sea water distillation and the presence of brackish water in the sewage which has been stored in above ground reservoirs. The higher chloride concentrations are a result of the dual supply of brackish and fresh water. The brackish water contains a high concentration of chloride ions which subsequently are found in the sewage. The high sewage and air temperatures favour rapid microbial growth and rapid oxygen depletion. Sewages are therefore likely to turn anaerobic in the sewage system which explains the presence of hydrogen sulphide.

The diurnal and annual variations described in Chapter 4 will apply to similar sites in other locations. The very hot summer months will produce an increased water demand even from a constant community. Per capita water supply figures of 100 l/d in winter can increase by more than 50% during the hottest months[1]. This will be accompanied by higher sewage temperatures and higher hydrogen sulphide concentrations (Table 16.1).

Table 16.1   *Sewage characteristics in a hot dry climate (Kuwait)*

	Jan. 1975	Aug. 1975
B.O.D$_5$ mg/l	189−673	197−813
S.S. mg/l	132−1006	120−1420
Ammonia mg/l	19.8−67.5	35.1−51.3
Organic nitrogen mg/l	4.9−16.8	14.0−37.8
Nitrate ions mg/l	Nil.	Nil.
Chloride ions mg/l	1080−2900	1182−1460
Hydrogen sulphide mg/l	1.3−5.7	13.6−20.2
pH	7.3−8.5	7.2−7.5
Temperature °C	21.0−25.0	30.0−33.0

This type of information should be collected for likely sewage treatment works and account made of it during subsequent design and operation of the works

16.2   Effluent standards

The conventional Royal Commission effluent standards have found world-wide acceptance. The commonly quoted 20 mg/l B.O.D.$_5$ and 30 mg/l S.S. is often required as an effluent standard. It should however be remembered that even the Royal Commission suggested several different effluent standards and did not recommend the 20 : 30 standard for general use. Local conditions or customs can cause more stringent criteria; pollution of underground water or religious objections to polluting certain water courses have led to strict controls while the use of effluents for irrigation can be beneficial and the presence of large rivers as a receiving water or a sea outfall into tidal waters can lead to a more relaxed standard.

The most likely variation from the general recommendations of the Royal Commission (Chapter 3) concerns the volume of sewage to be treated. The concept of fully treating up to three times D.W.F. with provision for some treatment up to six times D.W.F. clearly allows for the presence of storm water. Therefore, in climates which have very low rainfall (less than 100 mm per annum has been reported), infiltration can be ignored and the flow to receive treatment can be considerably reduced. It is therefore not unreasonable and is often cheaper to require full treatment for only 2 D.W.F. In the case of small sewage treatment works, these considerations are usually less critical than for larger works but do suggest that plants can be smaller than previously stated.

16.3   Effect of temperature on bioxidation

The problems associated with sewage treatment processes in hot climates are mainly the result of the increased rate of reaction of both oxidizing and reducing reactions with higher liquid temperatures. These effects may be compounded by local geographical conditions such as increased altitude or by the presence of extraordinarily large amounts of conservative ions such as chloride ion.

The basic reaction rate constant for sewage increases with increasing temperature. Equation 16.1 (below) has been suggested to describe this variation

$$k_T = k_{20} \, 1.047^{(T-20)} \ldots \tag{16.1}$$

where:

k_T is the rate constant for the bioxidation of sewage at temperature $T°C$;

k_{20} is the rate constant at 20°C.

If the rate constant is assumed to be 0.17/d at 20°C the rate constants for 10°C and 35°C can be seen to be 0.11/d and 0.34/d respectively. This represents a tripling of the mean reaction rate. A rule of thumb which is often used is that the reaction rate will double for every 9 or 10°C. The effect of this doubling of the reaction rate can mean not only that the rate of oxygen demand is greater but that the sewage arrives at the works in a reduced state. Hence the large concentrations of sulphide ion (Table 16.1). Although the retention time in the sewers would be expected to be considerably shorter in small communities it should be realized that residence times in pumping wells, etc., at high ambient temperatures will produce a sewage which will exert an immediate high oxygen demand on the works.

16.4   Treatment Processes
The activated sludge, percolating filter and rotating biological filter processes described in the earlier chapters can all be used. Additionally, in conditions of strong sunlight, oxidation ponds can be used.

16.4.1   Oxidation ponds
While the predominate microbiological type in the previous processes has been bacteria, in oxidation ponds there are considerable numbers of algae. Under the influence of sunlight algae can produce oxygen while utilizing carbon dioxide and nutrient materials (phosphate, nitrate, etc.). Aeration is therefore provided by the algae and usually by natural surface aeration. There is some exchange of materials between the algae and bacteria, waste products from one serving as useful materials for the other.

The most common type of oxidation pond is a facultative pond which is aerobic in its surface layers, anaerobic at the bottom where a sludge accumulates and has a central depth which can be aerobic or anaerobic depending upon conditions. It is beyond the scope of this volume to treat in detail the design, construction and operation of this or other types of oxidation pond; more precise information is readily available[2,3]; a few general points are relevant. The design criteria[2,3] usually refer to the temperature and/or sunlight intensity of the site and compute loadings and sizes of ponds. The retention time in a facultative pond is often of the order of 28 days with a pond depth of approximately 2 m. The ponds therefore cover a large area and the problems of pollution of underground waters by leaking ponds and of insects and odours can be significant. The ponds can provide a low cost, low maintenance, easily operated treatment facility and are generally considered to provide an effluent which has a very low bacterial count.

16.4.2   Settlement processes

The increased rate of reaction discussed in Section 16.3 is not confined to the sewage bioxidation process. The production of rising sludge due to gas formation in settlement tanks will also be increased with increasing temperature. In Britain in the summer months it is often necessary to desludge primary settlement tanks at intervals between 4 days and one week depending on the characteristics of the sewage and the settlement process. In climates where the sewage temperature is above 30°C, the rate of gasification of the settled sewage would be increased to the point where daily desludging would be required. As the temperature varies with locality a general rule could be suggested that for each rise of 9°C tanks should be desludged twice as often.

The effect of increased temperature on the efficiency of settlement is small since the major variable affected is viscosity. The overflow rates and weir overflow rates at maximum flow adopted for hot climates are often identical with those for conventional British practice given in Chapter 7. The retention times used in Britain cannot be adopted as easily. Primary settlement in Britain suggests a retention time of 4.5 to 6 hours at 1 D.W.F. The effect of this with an ambient sewage temperature of 30 to 35°C would be to greatly increase the initial oxygen demand on the subsequent secondary treatment system. Fortunately, in some countries, because the rainfall is more predictable, the flow requiring full treatment may be less, e.g. up to 2 D.W.F. This reduces the variation in flow to be accommodated by the settlement tank and simplifies the choice of design criteria. If the maximum flow is to be 2 D.W.F. a retention time at 35°C of 1 hour at this flow would remove a considerable amount of the polluting load and only dictate a retention time of 2 hours at 1 D.W.F. In Britain there has been a considerable change in the last two decades towards shorter primary settlement tank retention times, in certain cases tanks designed for a conventional retention time of 1½ hours at 3.5 D.W.F. are receiving 6 D.W.F. and are proving to be satisfactory. Viewed in this light the above suggestion of 1–2 hours retention time for a primary settlement tank is reasonable.

The settlement of activated sludge is in the context of this book usually carried out in package plants and will be discussed in the next section.

16.4.3   Activated sludge process

Assuming that the sewage is to be treated, without primary settlement, by a package plant, one of the major problems is that associated with aeration. The effect of increased temperature reduces the saturation concentration of oxygen in the liquid, but fortunately increases the mass transport coefficient.

Downing[4] has suggested that within the range 10–30°C the two effects cancel themselves out. The increased oxidation rate however means that in any system involving plug flow, the initial oxygen demand will be very high. This will also be increased by the possibility of a highly anaerobic sewage being received at the works. The increased reaction rate constant means that the retention time will be reduced. However, the amount of oxygen required per capita to oxidize the B.O.D. will be approximately the same as in Britain. The net effect of the above conditions will be to argue for an increased blower capacity to allow for the oxidation of the sulphide and the other materials in the sewage. This probably represents between 5 and 10% extra capacity requirement.

In certain countries the effect of altitude is quite considerable. An increased altitude affects the oxygen saturation value and therefore effectively reduces the capacity of the aerator. It has been suggested, therefore, that capacity of the blowers should be increased by approximately 4% for each 300 m increase in height.

One problem which may be encountered in hot climates is the production of a fine, poor settling activated sludge caused by a combination of increased temperature and overaeration. It is therefore better to reduce the retention time from the very long aeration periods suggested by CP 302: 1972 for Extended Aeration works. The use of dissolved oxygen electrodes as a monitoring device for commissioning package plants is much more necessary in hot climates to ensure operation between the twin pitfalls of initial anaerobic conditions and overaeration. Plants which utilize a plug flow regime rather than a completely mixed system can clearly adjust the oxygen levels more easily, providing additional aeration at the beginning of the aeration process to meet the high initial demand and with lower rates of aeration in later stages to prevent overaeration. The settlement of the activated sludge from a package plant will not occur at a significantly greater rate due to increased temperature. However, the production of an anaerobic sludge with consequent problems in the aeration and settlement stages will need to be guarded against. Long settlement periods of 8 hours or so which may occur in large scale British plants are totally inapplicable. Package plants which use the principle of gravity return of settled activated sludge to the aeration compartment may give rise to problems due to the onset of anaerobic conditions. It is much better to have a positive sludge return system and to use an oxidation – reduction potential probe or a dissolved oxygen meter to monitor the sludge condition in the secondary tank. The overflow rates (having allowed for any scumming device) used in British practice appear to be satisfactory.

The use of aerobic stabilization of waste activated sludges is satisfactory in hot climates with an increased rate of reduction in S.S.

16.4.4 *Percolating filters*
Several equations have been produced relating the purification achieved in percolating filter installations at different temperatures, and attempts have been

made also to improve the efficiency of the process in Britain by covering the filter and thus retaining some of the heat produced in bacterial action. This has usually not been thought worthwhile due to the high cost of covering such a large area. The Galler Gotaas formula[5] suggests that the volume of filter media is proportional to $T^{0.15}$ where T is the temperature in °C. This indicates a relatively weak dependence of media volume upon temperature, if the volumes of media for populations of up to 1000 are calculated according to CP 302 as modified by Nicholl[6], i.e. Volume = $1.5\,P^{0.8}$ where P is the population. Assuming that this is sufficient for a mean yearly sewage temperature of 10°C, the effects, on the volumes of media required at 20°C and 30°C, are shown in Table 16.2. The volume reductions are usually less than 20% at the higher temperatures.

Table 16.2   *Effect of increased temperature on volume of filter media*

Population	Media requirement (m^3) at different temperatures[5,6]		
	10°C	20°C	30°C
50	34.3	30.9	29.0
100	59.7	53.8	50.6
500	216.0	195.0	183.5
1000	377.0	340.0	319.5

Rotating biological filters appear to work well and produce good quality effluents in hot climates. Theoretically it should be possible to reduce the number of discs under such circumstances however little information is available on this topic.

16.5   Sludge treatment

The drying of waste activated sludges occurs more rapidly in hot climates with lower humidities. Providing the sludges have cracked, even significant rainfall will have little effect on the sludge. In middle eastern countries activated sludges will tend to dry within a week although they may produce a misleading dry surface appearance in a shorter period of time. In countries where the rainfall is intense over short periods it is worthwile considering some form of covering for the beds.

Primary sludges dry much quicker in middle eastern countries; however, the odour problems are quite considerable. One interesting method of overcoming this problem has been used by the Inka Division of Johnson Construction Ltd. who have adopted an aerobic digestion system for primary sludges similar to that incorporated in their Inka Bioreactors for waste activated sludge. This method has been used with some success in the middle east. The high concentrations of grease and fats present in primary sludge have led to a surface build-up in the digester. This problem has been overcome by using a surface scum removal system. The other difficulty is to keep large materials particularly of faecal origin in suspension – some form of maceration is advantageous. After such digestion for a period of up to 18 days, the sludge is reported to dewater easily on drying beds with little odour nuisance. Anaerobic digestion, providing a minimum of external heat can also be useful but is rarely feasible at small plants. Sludge pressing or filtering processes can also be used provided that odour and insect problems can be overcome.

16.6 Conclusions

Since the term hot climates can be interpreted to include a very large percentage of the earth's habitable land area the above discussion has inevitably tended to be general rather than specific. The importance of insect and odour problems cannot be overstressed nor can the need for continued efficient operation and maintenance. Where specific instances or problems have been discussed these have tended to be in the context of middle eastern countries. The authors make no apology for this since for the next decade at least it is probable that this area will be the focus of much export effort.

References
[1] *Statistics of the Ministry of Electricity and Water,* Kuwait, 1975.
[2] *Waste Stabilization Ponds,* E. F. Gloyna, W.H.O. Geneva, 1971.
[3] *Waste Stabilization Ponds, Design, Construction and Operation in India,* S. J. Archeivala, J. S. S. Lakshminarayana, S. R. Alagarsamy and C. A. Sastry, Central Pub. Health Eng. Res. Inst., Nagpur, 1970.
[4] A. L. DOWNING, Aeration in the activated sludge process, *J. Inst. Pub. Hlt. Eng.* LIX, 1960, 80–117.
[5] J. M. BAKER and Q. B. GRAVES, Recent approaches to trickling filter designs, *J. San. Eng. Div. Proc. Am. Soc. Civ. Eng.* **94**, 1968, 65–84.
[6] E. H. NICOLL, Aspects of small water pollution control works, *J. Inst. Publ. Hlth. Engs.,* Issue **12**, Nov. 1974, 185–211.

Suggested further reading
[1] M. R. N. SHEPHARD and H. A. HAWKES, Laboratory studies on the effects of temperature on the accumulation of solids in biological filters, *Wat. Pollut. Control* 1976, 58–72.

Index